CARE
FOR THE
CARER

CARE FOR THE CARER

Make Life Easier, Happier, More Fulfilling—For You _and_ the Elderly Person You Look After

CHRISTINE ORTON

FOREWORD BY JUDITH OLIVER,
PRESIDENT, CARERS NATIONAL ASSOCIATION

THORSONS PUBLISHING GROUP

First published 1989

©CHRISTINE ORTON 1989

British Library Cataloguing in Publication Data

Orton, Christine
Care for the carer: make life easier,
happier, more fulfilling – for you *and* your
elderly relative.
1. Great Britain. Old persons. Home care –
Manuals
I. Title
649.8

ISBN 0-7225-1639-8

Illustrated by Jane Bottomley

*Published by Thorsons Publishing Group Limited,
Wellingborough, Northamptonshire, NN8 2RQ, England*

Printed in Great Britain by Billing & Sons Limited, Worcester

1 3 5 7 9 10 8 6 4 2

Contents

A carer's experience

'After living in Scotland all my years I've had to move to London owing to my husband having a stroke. I am 63 years of age and my husband 67. I've been caring for him now since June 1983 and still haven't come to terms with it. We had so much planned for retiring and then this happened. Believe me, it doesn't matter how many of a family you have, it doesn't help. It hurts so much and you're so lonely that I'm afraid of what I'll do at times. No one understands except the ones with experience. All the doctors and social workers can't ease your pain. I feel I'm living in a limbo world and don't know which way to turn. I've never had anyone that I could really describe my feelings to and talk the way I would like. The hurt inside you is indescribable. I used to see people with strokes and say how sorry I was. If I'd known then what I know now, how I could have helped them. Every time I look at my husband it's like someone is piercing something through my heart. I don't cry so much now as I used to outwardly, but inwardly I seem to be crying all the time. To see a big strong man being struck down is heart-rending. He was such a hard-working man and so independent, and now he has to depend on me so much it must be terrible. I'm suffering a lot with my back, and with the help my husband needs, this doesn't help either. I also broke my leg very badly last year which made things worse. I think it worries my husband so much we're not as close as we used to be. We seem to be growing apart which once again is another worry. If there was a stroke club here he could go to which would give us a break from one another for a few hours, this would help us. But there isn't. It's just a life of fear unless you have the money for help which we haven't. I just live in a world of my own at times and dream. But at other times I feel life is finished and doesn't hold any meaning for both of us. This is not a dramatic version of life, this is precisely how the stroke has affected us. If it weren't for my husband's will to fight, I think I'd have done something desperate long ago.'

Foreword

While the work of caring for disabled, sick or elderly relatives at home is one that has taken place since time began, those carrying out this essential and humanitarian role have been entirely disregarded.

One so often hears the cry, 'but *no one* cares for their own these days!' that it would be tempting to believe that this is the case. Yet the facts utterly belie these deeply held misconceptions.

In the census of 1901, it was discovered that only 5 per cent of elderly and disabled people were cared for in hospitals, homes or other institutions. Despite policies of decanting from the large-scale hospitals, the percentage of people in non-family settings remains the same today. In other words, families are caring for their dependent relatives in exactly the same proportions as they were 90 odd years ago, but demographic changes mean that the *numbers* being cared for at home are considerably larger than at any time in the past.

Firstly, people generally live to a greater age than before. Although there have always been those who survived to extreme old age, the majority died in infancy or up to late middle age. This was the case until the middle of the twentieth century, when the discovery of drugs such as insulin and penicillin saved lives that would have otherwise been lost. High-tech medical developments, such as pacemakers and life-support machines, have meant that death need not necessarily be inevitable.

This situation, happy as it may usually be, has brought with it a vastly increased need for care of elderly people, both by the State and by families. However, this need has come at a time when welfare services are unable to cope with even the smaller numbers of the recent past.

Secondly, medical advances have contributed to far higher social expectations. Not only, then, are people living longer, but they and their carers are asking for a standard of living that is more than mere existence.

Families today then are, in fact, caring *more* than ever before. They are looking after more elderly and disabled relatives and they are doing it for considerably longer.

The carers' movement

However much families have cared, they have always been the 'invisible' arm of the welfare state. Unacknowledged, unrewarded, unthanked, they have had just two options – carry on or give up. For most, the latter is unthinkable. Many may wish to, but few, short of collapsing, feel able to opt out. They look at the quality of life in institutions, many of which seem to have changed little since Charles Dickens' time, and decide that that couldn't be for anybody dear to them. Even when they have found somewhere suitable, the cost and the difficulties of arranging for their relatives to be admitted, have made many decide to carry on caring for them themselves.

The first indication that carers were beginning to think of themselves for once, came in 1964, when the National Council for the Single Woman and Her Dependants (later the National Council for Carers and Their Elderly Dependants) was formed. In 1981, another organization came into being – the Association of Carers. In May 1988, the two merged to become the new Carers National Association with a brief to represent all carers, no matter what the age or disability of the dependant.

The existence of these organizations led to increased interest in the difficulties experienced by carers, though one could also be cynical and say that interest did not emerge from the government or from local authorities until policies of community care, introduced in the 1970s, made many officials panic and begin to wonder where all these 'community carers' were going to come from.

Apart from the Invalid Care Allowance regulations, until

1986, there was no mention of carers in any British legislation – we were non-people – but, that year, Tom Clarke MP won the Private Member's Bill ballot and this led to the Disabled Persons (Services, Consultation and Representation) Act 1986. Section 8 of this Act brings carers a very small, but none-theless welcome, entitlement. When an assessment is being made of the abilities and needs of their dependant, the 'ability of the carer to continue to provide care' has to be taken into consideration. Small beer, perhaps, but a breakthrough for a long-forgotten group.

One of the first problems in acknowledging carers and their needs has been that no one had, until June 1988, even the remotest idea of how many carers there were in the British Isles. One could argue that this didn't really matter, since any carer who approached a statutory or voluntary agency for help should be entitled to receive it, but the bureaucratic mentality is to count heads before providing services. Very rough 'guesstimates' were made and in 1981 it was thought that 1.3 million people cared for someone who required intensive support and a further 3–4 million gave considerable help to a relative who was frail or otherwise physically or mentally dependent.

In 1986, the Office of Population Censuses and Surveys asked, for the first time, questions about the caring respon-sibilities of interviewees in the General Household survey. The figures revealed that many more than this were entitled to call themselves 'carers'. One in every seven of those ques-tioned were undoubtedly providing care for a disabled or elderly relative or friend. In some age groups (the 40s and 50s) as many as one in every two women is a carer.

What happens now is anyone's guess. Carers would undoubtedly fare rather better than they do now if there were only, say, 50,000 of them in the whole country. What does one do with 6 or 7 *million*?

There is no question that carers will have to be their own advocates, since, if we are quiet and good, no one will ever take any notice of us.

Christine Orton's book may well be a start for many carers. She writes in a most readable and down-to-earth way. Her book does not, as so many in this field, deter by either its weight or its language. Here, one feels, is someone who has been there herself, who understands and does not preach.

Above all, the book carries one vital message. Carers are *important*. We have neglected ourselves for too long. We do no one any favours by acting like this. They, and we, deserve better.

JUDITH OLIVER

Introduction

Talking to a great number of carers of elderly people over the past year or so, I have seen how many of you carry out this task willingly, efficiently and with deep affection, in spite of all the difficulties involved.

There can be a great sense of satisfaction and reward in taking care of someone you have loved and been close to for many years, and who in turn may have looked after you – as parent, partner or friend – in years gone by, but, hearing your experiences, I have also seen the great sacrifices you make. In caring for another, carers often forget to care for themselves, gradually giving up all interests and friends, and putting aside their own needs in preference to someone elses.

This book is written to try and right the balance a little. Though it may be necessary and inevitable for you as carers to spend an enormous amount of time looking after someone who is elderly and perhaps ill and dependent, it is equally important for you to look after yourselves, too. Your health, in mind as well as body, is vital not only for the person you take care of but for your own sake as well.

Even though this book is therefore primarily for the carers, some chapters do concentrate on the needs of the older people because, by finding solutions to their problems, carers can have happier, more satisfying lives, too. If the older person is physically comfortable and emotionally secure, then you as carer are more comfortable and secure as well.

The information in these pages covers the emotional, practical and financial difficulties that can arise. Many carers feel very alone and often do not have easy access to services, sources of advice or financial assistance. As some of the case histories show, money may be so short that this affects every aspect of life. By reading how other carers have found help and ways of coping, I hope you will be helped yourself.

Unfortunately the back-up support that carers at home so desperately need from professionals is often simply not available. NHS cutbacks mean that services, far from being on the increase, are actually decreasing in many areas. There are some shining examples of good practice, however. A home-visiting scheme in the Brent area, for instance, caters especially for the needs of the Afro-Caribbean and Asian people in the area. There is the hospital in Sussex that concentrates on rehabilitating older people so that they continue to be as independent as possible. There is the Suffolk bed-rotation scheme which means that elderly people can automatically spend short spells in a hospital or residential home while carers get a break. My hope is that this book will be read by professional as well as lay carers, and that the sort of examples of support schemes mentioned will stimulate other local authorities to set up or fund similar services and projects in their areas. At present the provision is patchy, but at least some authorities are showing the way.

Finally I would like to thank the many voluntary organizations and individuals who have helped in the preparation of this book, most especially Kathy Weir of the Family Welfare Association and Judith Oliver and Jill Pitkeathley of the Carers National Association. Their advice and guidance as people very experienced in this field has been invaluable. Through them I was able to reach the many carers of elderly people whose day-by-day experiences and tips form the basis of this book. Much of what is said in the following pages is not only *for* carers but *by* carers. My thanks to you all for being so open and for sharing your feelings and knowledge so generously.

CHRISTINE ORTON

CHAPTER 1
What caring really means

'Other carers understand and I feel consolation in having found our little support group. We are all so different but have the same emotions – isolation, guilt and conflict.'

'The problem is, whenever I try to explain my troubles it sounds as though I am complaining, which is not the case.'

Speaking for yourselves

People caring for an elderly relative or friend at home often feel extremely isolated. But though you may not realize it, you are certainly not alone. Thousands of others are also carers – in fact more today than ever before. Yet it is only quite recently that the loneliness and the needs of carers have become more widely talked about. Until now carers have felt alone because, as well as not knowing much about each other, few people outside knew about them and their difficulties, either.

This has been partly due to a conflict of loyalties among carers themselves. Kathy Weir, a counsellor who helped set up a support group through the Family Welfare Association, discovered that carers find it difficult to speak openly about their lives and their caring role when they are looking after someone they love:

'Particularly when you have other ties of gratitude and duty – to your mother or husband, another close relative or a friend, people who you have promised to cherish in sickness and in health – talking about how difficult the task is can seem like a betrayal.

'However much you love the person you're caring for, sometimes the sheer task can make you feel like screaming and wishing they weren't with you. "But what is my relative going to think if I say I'm going to a group to talk about them?" they ask, "Isn't it selfish to go and talk about myself? I just need to get on with it, not talk about it." '

On top of this most carers are not used to being encouraged to unburden themselves and find it difficult to think about themselves, let alone talk. The services, the benefits, the aids and appliances, often the housing itself, is for the relative's benefit rather than for the carer's.

'The first question most people ask is how is your mum or your auntie or your husband?', says Kathie, 'They don't ask after *you*. Occupational therapists, home helps, district nurses come to look after your relative, not you.

'Often your questions and anxieties aren't properly addressed by medical and other staff, and you feel ignored and belittled. But at the same time you are being asked to do one of the most demanding and responsible tasks it's possible to do.'

Uncomplainingly carrying out these tasks is what most carers have been doing for years. They do it with great devotion and efficiency, but, all too often, they sacrifice their own needs and well-being in the process.

Fortunately Kathy and others like her have been able to persuade those in their support groups to both think and talk about themselves. These carers discovered their own voice and realized that by discussing their problems together they are able to let go of some of their negative feelings and gain help from each other. There is no disloyalty to the one they care for in that – in fact in the end they find that sharing their lives gives them greater strength to cope with the demands of caring.

Some typical situations

The reasons why carers find themselves in this role in the first place obviously varies from person to person, but those who have talked to me, both individually and at support group meetings, and contacted me by letter, seem to fall into four main categories:

- The single person still living in the family home who cares for dependant parents, other relatives or friends.
- The husband, wife or close friend who cares for a partner in his or her own home.
- The married son, daughter or other relative or friend who has the older person to live with the family.
- The relative or friend who cares for the elderly person while both remain in their separate homes.

The reasons for the older person's dependence also vary, of course, and with them the strains that being a carer may bring.

For some the disablement is purely physical. Arthritis, a stroke or some other disorder may mean that the elderly person is unable to get around easily and may need help in doing the simplest tasks, from going to the toilet or eating a meal to getting in and out of bed.

Others are affected mentally and emotionally, perhaps through senile dementia, including Alzheimer's disease, which afflicts so many older people. Some have visual or hearing handicaps, others problems with speech and communication.

For some older people, such as those who have had a stroke, results may be both physical *and* mental, and this can be the hardest burden of all for carers. Not only do they take the strain of lifting, carrying, bathing, feeding and a thousand other physical demands for that person, they may also lack the emotional comfort and companionship they once shared. Because speech may be a problem, there may also be a lack of easy communication and intellectual stimulation.

The following case histories reflect these situations and difficulties – though, typically, one carer pointed out when telling me his that: 'The problem is, whenever I try to explain my troubles, it sounds as though I am complaining, which is not the case.'

The single daughter

Joyce was single, an only child and already living at home

when her widowed mother with an arthritic hip had a fall and started to need full-time care.

'I gave up my job to be at home, which also meant I only left my mother for shopping trips. We were lucky to get the full attendance allowance for her, so managed financially.

'I had many problems in lifting my mother in and out of bed and onto the commode, for as she got older her legs got stiff and pushing her about I broke open a bad spot on her back. It gave her so much pain in sitting on her chair and also in bed.

'Later she lost the use of her legs altogether and Parkinson's disease was discovered. This crippled her legs and she became incontinent which distressed her as she was still sound in mind.

'The doctor got in the district nurses and they were a marvellous bunch of people who brought me free everything I could possibly need for mother's convenience and comfort. They would come twice or even three times day and night, weekends and holidays.

'Even so, being a carer is very restricting and demanding, and it makes you very tired if you are the only one. I did not mind, but many would not have liked the restrictions on their outings. I only went out to shop for the first two years. After that I had shopping brought in to me and didn't leave home at all.

'Mother died aged 90 years and three months. However, she was at home with me by her side, and it was all very peaceful, thank the Lord.'

Husband and wife

John is one of the many carers looking after a partner who has become ill. He and his wife Jill had enjoyed some happy years together after his retirement, touring in a caravan abroad. Then Jill had a stroke and their life completely changed.

'We live in sheltered housing, a long way from our family. I have to care for my wife in every way – dressing, washing, helping on and off the toilet, lifting in and out of bed and her chair. I do all the housework, cooking, cleaning and so on.

'We have a home help 1½ hours a week and my wife also gets bed baths once a week if she is lucky, but we are never sure whether the bath lady is coming or not. I could not risk getting her in or out of the bath on my own, not even with mechanical aids. We seldom see a district nurse, we see the doctor if we need him and my wife goes into hospital twice a year for 14 days to give me a rest.

'My biggest burden is the loss of personal liberty and choice of recreation. I have abandoned golf and fishing, mainly because of the impossibility of finding someone capable of caring for my severely handicapped partner.

'Various organizations try to make a carer's life more bearable, but I feel sure that most of us are unable to make use of these opportunities because we cannot find sitters capable of caring for our loved ones in our absence – and what's the use of time off if you are worrying all the time?'

Caring in the family

Mary is a married woman whose father moved in with her family after he had had a stroke. His own home was in an isolated area five miles from the shops and main services and 60 miles from his daughter and family.

'In common with many areas it was not the practice to hospitalize stroke patients who were over 60. The decision to move him in with us was the only feasible way of coping with my father, plus three children under six, a husband and puppies.

'We discovered there were three main areas of tension. First I resented the lack of the evenings with the children and my husband. The needs of the extra generation at the end of the day made me feel very torn and tense. Secondly, finances needed to be more formally settled and properly handled to avoid having to ask for money or find that we were being overpaid for small tasks, especially those done by the children. Thirdly, we needed the children's summer holidays, so that we could continue to go camping and have the day treats as we always had done.'

As it happened, Mary's father made a good recovery from his stroke and was able to move into a nearby flat on his own in sheltered accommodation. He lived there happily for three years until he became ill again and had to move back with the family.

He remained with them for the last seven years of his life.

Travelling to care

Margaret is another married carer, but her parents have mostly stayed in their own home and she has therefore had to travel long distances to be with them.

In her case much of the conflict has arisen from trying to be in three places at once – at home with her husband, at home with her parents and continuing to work at her job.

'It started one Christmas. My mum and dad came to stay with us for a few weeks and, because dad was ill, stayed on for three months. Then they moved to a new bungalow, with mum taking on more responsibility.

'Then mum had her first stroke and ended up in hospital. Later she had another stroke. Dad was deteriorating again and came to live with my husband and me. The stage was reached where I could no longer cut myself in so many pieces and I decided to give up work.

'What with caring for dad and travelling backwards and forwards visiting mum every day I did not have time to think of the repercussions that giving up work might bring. The hardest has been having to rely on my husband financially, not only to feed and clothe me, but to help keep my car on the road.

'Mum and dad are now back home and I am still travelling to care. After all this time I feel I am the person who needs help. I am under the doctor for what he thinks is a stress-related condition. Mum and dad have a home help, meals on wheels, a community visitor and day care, but my resources are low mentally, physically and financially.'

Some shared problems

As well as graphically illustrating some of the common problems that lead to caring in the first place, these experiences also highlight the sort of difficulties people who are looking after an elderly person share.

● **Physical stress**
The wear and tear resulting from a daily round of lifting,

bathing, toiletting and so on, plus the added strains of travelling, keeping a job and looking after home and family

- **Mental stress**
  Emotions, mind and moods can be affected by the responsibility, worry and isolation, and also the illogical behaviour of older people who have become mentally frail. There may be conflicts, too, with other people in the family

- **Financial stress**
  Caring is expensive in itself, with the extra cost of heating, washing, special diets, etc. Many carers also have to give up work and may not receive any of the benefits for which they are eligible. A large number exist in a state of real poverty.

- **Social stress**
  There can be loss of contact with the outside world and increasing loneliness. It may be impossible to get out, others don't call, and there can be loss of a relationship with the older person because of mental and/or physical disability.

These problems can build into a vicious circle that is hard to break – one difficulty leading to another and then round again.

As a report by the Association of Carers called *Caring and Mental Health* shows, isolation is often seen as the main trigger for this. The frequent loss of friends, family, status, income and independence all mean that the carer and cared for can get locked away into a world of their own. This can lead to anger and resentment in both, and then guilt for feeling this way about someone you love.

The guilt may then lead to greater sacrifices on the part of the carers to compensate. You are then less able to have some sort of independent life, your self-esteem may fall lower and lead to even greater isolation.

Some solutions

This type of vicious circle is discussed in more detail in Chapter

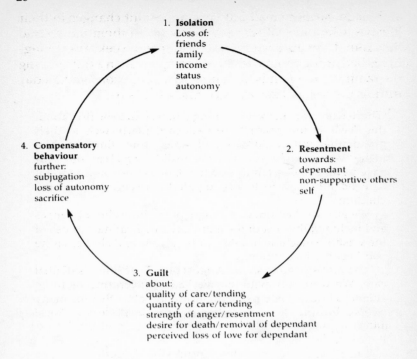

The vicious circle that carers often fall prey to while coping with the demands that caring involves.

6 with ideas for breaking it so that carers can establish a life and confidence of their own, while still giving their dependant all the care they need. At this stage it's probably enough to say that there *are* solutions and that many carers eventually hit upon answers to their own particular problems. For instance John (mentioned earlier) who, because he was busy looking after his wife missed his independence and interests, has taken up writing.

> 'Luckily I have discovered, rather late in life, the ability to invent and write stories. So, for a few hours each week, I am able to sit down at my typewriter, oblivious for a while of our troubles.'

Mary's family learned from their first experience of caring

and made various small but very important changes in their lifestyle when her father came to live with them the second time round. For instance, he agreed to spend weekday evenings in his bedsitting room with his evening meal on a tray, joining the family at weekends, for any special occasions and all day during the week if he wished. Mary explains:

'There were days in the beginning when I had to be firm about this. Two of the children related particularly well to their grandfather and would frequently spend some time with him in the evenings in his room so that he did not feel cast out. This gave us time to be a family and for all of us this was important as I did not want to feel so divided between dad and the children.

'We also worked out dad's share of the household finances and included the cost of the extra daytime heating and use of the washing machine to cater for his sheets and clothes, as he had become incontinent.

'Dad also agreed to spend August of each year in residential care. We were fortunate that he had sufficient means to be able to afford private residential care. I realize that for many people the problem of finding a suitable place in a local authority home would make things much more difficult than they were for us.

'I also realize that most people moving an elderly relative in with them do not have the opportunity of a trial ten months first, but I hope that points emerging from our experience may help other carers create a pattern that will help them cope with their elderly dependant.

'I know that putting the unity of my own family uppermost was the most important thing. In so doing, every member of the family supported me, in his or her own way, to care fully for dad.'

Lack of services

Not every carer finds answers for all their problems and certainly not straight away. It can be a matter of trial with some error before discovering what may be helpful and where to look for it.

Certain problems, for instance, can be overcome or made

worse depending on where you live. Most carers quoted in this chapter so far have been very satisfied with the help they have received from local authority health and social services departments, but this is by no means always the case. Many carers battle on year after year with little or no support, particularly if they live in a remote, rural part of the country or in an area where there are inadequate services. Their position is made worse by lack of finances, when they cannot afford to pay for help either.

As we will see in later chapters, there are other more complex reasons why carers have to manage alone, including the older people themselves rejecting outsiders coming in, but in some cases there is literally no one to call on.

One particularly sad letter I received reflects the desperation of carers who find themselves without any means of support. The writer is an only daughter, who looks after her 84-year-old mother, registered partially sighted and almost unable to walk:

> 'Now she rarely goes out, and never without me. Neither of us have a friend locally and we have no close relatives to call. Frankly ours is a pretty bleak, isolated, hopeless sort of life.
>
> 'Neighbours are not at all friendly and in three years not one has even offered us a lift or a cup of tea even though we asked them in when we first came here. As my mother is not yet totally blind, no social worker calls and the doctor is indifferent to any problems.
>
> 'This seems a very poor area for carers and their charges. There is no carers' support scheme run by volunteers and I truly do not know what mum would do if I were to die first. There is not one solitary soul she could call on for support. I am her only prop. I long for help but it never comes.'

Finding support

What this carer and so many like her need is a local support group where they can meet and talk to other carers and also find skilled counsellors and advice.

Margaret, who you will recall, has to travel to look after her parents, found it was a support group that gave her the courage to continue.

> 'Other carers understand. I feel consolation in having found our little group. We are all so different, but share the same emotions – isolation, guilt and conflict.'

In one London borough the local Community Health Council and Age Concern branch carried out a survey among carers living in the area to find out exactly what their needs were. Top of the list were the following:

- A regular break from caring so that they could return to it with their batteries recharged.
- Access to information on what practical and financial help is available and on disorders suffered by their elderly dependants.
- Someone to talk to and share experiences with, both positive and negative, emotional and practical.

The survey found that one in five carers had no one to talk to at all. Along with the need for local authority schemes to provide qualified professional help and respite care, they recommended support groups as an urgent requirement.

Those who go to such groups often find that this is a turning point in their lives. One Sussex group started with just five members and has now blossomed to more than 20, with other groups starting up. Two members tell what the group has meant to them:

> 'As a carer the group has meant new friends. After working in a large establishment it was this I missed most of all. Being able to go along to the group with my other half and meet people who are tolerant and patient without fear of embarrassment gave me a new life and a chance to be a little independent.'

> 'Being one of the founder members I have watched the group grow and develop. It has grown by bringing together complete strangers, but those strangers become friends and form together one happy band of carers.
> 'It has grown to form a companionship, caring for each other by visiting those unfortunate members who happen to be in hospital, holding fortnightly meetings with that

welcome cup of tea and cakes, organizing talks by guest
speakers and having discussion between ourselves.

'Thus we learn and increase our knowledge, making us
more understanding people.'

Catering for needs

Support groups vary in how they are organized. The Sussex
group, for example, is mainly for carers of elderly people who
are mentally frail and both the carer and the dependant relative or friend go along to the meetings.

'Initially it was thought that carers should come on their own
with a volunteer to sit with the cared for person at home', says
one member. 'Then we thought about using a smaller room
next to the main lounge in which volunteers could look after
the cared for so that, we thought, carers could have a
break.

'In the event it was found that the carers much preferred to
have their loved ones sit in on the meeting so that they could
keep a practised eye on them. Both obviously benefit from the
social mix and on no occasion have we experienced any
serious anti-social disruption.'

Other groups are only for the carers, and this obviously
makes it easier for members to talk more freely about their
feelings and various problems. It also allows a break from the
caring role and time for carers just to be themselves for a
while.

Some groups have counsellors, who either lead group discussions or are available on a one-to-one basis. This can be
particularly supportive when emotions are confused. A
skilled counsellor can lead the carer to sort things out and
find ways of approaching problems more positively.

Most groups invite speakers along to give practical advice
or information about the various disabilities and also about
the local authority services and welfare benefits available.

It can help to have other activities apart from those centring
on the subject of caring. Some groups share outings and even
holidays. The Sussex group has the use of a local authority
minibus so that members can travel as a party to local places

of interest. One support group I visited had invited the local RSPCA officer along to talk about his experiences. This was a refreshing change for carers who had little opportunity to get out or think about anything else but their dependant. Meetings like this widen horizons again and they return home refreshed.

Starting a group

Support groups start in a variety of ways. Some are set up by local social services departments, others by Age Concern branches, others through the national carers' organizations.

Some groups are held in local authority Day or Day Care Centres, some in church halls and community centres, some in sheltered housing, and many in the homes of group members. The accent is usually on self-help, members starting and running their own groups.

This means that though there may be backup from the local authority or voluntary organization involved, the group raises its own funds and members share the job of planning meetings and outings.

If you are a carer living in an area where there is as yet no support group, the answer might be to start your own. With so much else to do already, you might think you just could not cope with this, but the very process of putting their thoughts and energies into a new venture has made many carers feel *more* rather than less able to cope with their daily lives.

A GP, health visitor or community nurse may form the first link with other carers living nearby. A notice in the local day centre, hospital outpatients' department or doctor's surgery, plus a small advertisement or article in the local paper can also put you in touch.

The next step will be to get together for a meeting and decide amongst yourselves how to share the responsibilities of running the group and which professionals, if any, to involve. From such small beginnings many support groups have grown and now flourish.

Suddenly carers feel that they are putting their expertise and

How to start up a carers' support group

If there is no group in your area, why not start your own?
Use the following steps as a guide:

- Ask your GP, health visitor or community nurse
  where other carers in your area live to get some idea
  of how many people might be interested in a
  support group.
- Put up a poster in your local day centre, hospital outpatients' department or doctor's surgery, giving your
  telephone number or address.
- Put an advertisement or article in your local paper
  and see what kind of response you get.
- Once you have some replies, arrange a meeting.
- At the meeting discuss who will be doing what and
  which professionals, if any, you would all like to
  involve in the group.

experience to wider use, helping others as well as themselves
and at the same time finding new friends, interests and
knowledge. Hearing about other people's difficulties can put
your own into perspective, without in any way minimizing
their importance. To be able to pass on practical tips is also
very rewarding and it's surprising how much can be learned
from comparing notes. Self-help increases your own confidence as well as that of others. It gives a quality of mutual
support that only those who have experienced the same
problems and therefore really understand can offer each
other. 'We're becoming a sort of large family unit where
everyone genuinely cares about each other in quite down to
earth and practical ways', is how one carer puts it.

For some, especially elderly people in the ethnic minorities
settled in this country, such support groups can be their only
life-line. They learn through them what services and medical
help is available, and can get in touch again with their own
cultures and traditions.

Even if you cannot actually start or reach a support group, there is still a great deal of mutual support and information to be found through various organizations specializing in helping carers. They are all listed at the back of this book, but the main one is:

● **The Carers National Association**
This was formerly two separate organizations — The Association of Carers and The National Council for Carers and Their Elderly Dependants – but they have now merged into an umbrella organization for carers. The Association of Carers was formed in 1981 and has answered many thousands of enquiries from carers since then. The National Council for Carers and Their Elderly Dependants (NCCED) was once entirely devoted to the needs of single women looking after older relatives, but then widened its coverage to offer help to all those caring for elderly people. It was therefore logical for these organizations to join forces.

This organization and others like the Family Welfare Association and Age Concern can give help in setting up a local support group. They also issue leaflets, newsletters and other literature, which put carers in touch with each other and with the support services that are available. Through this sort of contact you realize that you are not alone after all – and this can be the first and most important step towards a better quality of life.

CHAPTER 2
Preparing for change

'It's like talking to someone else. We're pals now, not lovers. It hurts, but it's a question of having to accept it the way it is. I try to adapt to her.'

'My day with her never begins or ends, it is continuous. I love her very much, that's why I do it. It has been suggested many times that I should put her into a home. That to me is unthinkable.'

Making plans

Caring for someone is often the result of an emergency such as an accident or sudden illness like a stroke or heart attack. Other times the situation will creep up on you gradually, as an older person becomes physically or mentally less able, but whichever way dependence comes about, if at all possible it's very important to make some plans long before the need actually arises.

Family and friends should try and talk over with the older person the whole question of where and with whom caring takes place so that even when a sudden decision has to be taken, some plans have been made already. This may seem a rather morbid thing to do, but in the end it can lead to a far more satisfactory arrangement for everyone concerned, including the older person. He or she will have the opportunity to decide on where he or she would like to be and who with. Equally, the people most likely to do the caring can make their views known and, at an early stage, ensure that they are not left to do the job alone.

Since caring involves strains that are physical, mental and

financial, to work out ways of coping beforehand can mean
that when the time actually comes many potential problems
have already been dealt with.

Care in the community

What is fairly certain nowadays is that at some point in their
lives most people will find themselves caring for an older person for a period of time.

There are a variety of reasons for this. One is that because
of advances in medicine and material comforts, people are
living longer. Growing older does not have to mean growing
ill and dependent, and many in their sixties, seventies and
older enjoy a full active life. Others are not so lucky and
develop a disability.

In spite of a common belief that the extended family has
had its day and that people generally are not so caring, the
facts show this to be something of a myth. Family and friends
today show, as much as they ever did, a real desire to look
after elderly dependants if at all possible. At the same time
there has been a move over the last few years to what is called
'care in the community' which encourages the care of all ill or
disabled people, young as well as old, to take place at home,
rather than in a home, hospital or other institution. Most see
this as an enlightened approach. The problem is that the professional services that should also have moved out into the
community are lagging behind. Ideally, while older people
are able to enjoy family, friends and familiar surroundings in
later years, the people caring for them should receive professional support. As we've already seen, however, many
don't.

The hope is that this will change over the next few years
and that a sensible balance will be found. Having gone from
one extreme to another so quickly, a middle ground must be
established that allows more choice for both the carer and the
cared for. Ideally, community care should include:

● Small, locally based residential homes and night and day
  respite centres where older people can spend some of their

time. Their needs will be met and so will those of the carers.

- Teams of community nursing staff readily available, night as well as day, to give practical backup so that carers are not pushed to their limits.
- Cash support paid automatically, so that carers actually receive the billions of pounds they are at present saving the government by often doing their job virtually unaided.

A home from home

This sort of care in the community is the ideal for the future. As things stand at present, however, choices are limited by the services currently in existence. But when we are thinking ahead and deciding what to do when a relative or friend can't manage alone any more, it is important to remember that within these limitations there are still some choices to be made. For instance, both the younger and older generation need to consider whether living together is the best answer or whether some form of residential or sheltered accommodation would be more suitable.

Friends and relatives may automatically shy away from this possibility, feeling that they will be rejecting or 'dumping' someone dear to them. But some older people actually prefer the idea, knowing that there will be plenty of company, not so much responsibility and a certain amount of independence. They may think that they will be a 'burden' to friends and family. Equally, they may not want to be uprooted from their homes and perhaps move miles away to live with a daughter and son-in-law they have never got on very well with anyway.

While still mentally and physically able they should have the opportunity to make these views known. Nor do those close to them need to feel guilty if they opt for being independent. The younger generation can still play an active and supportive part in older people's lives taking them on holidays and away for weekends, visiting regularly and making their love and interest strongly felt.

Some suitable alternatives

The types of accommodation available fall into the following main categories:

- **Sheltered accommodation**
  This term covers bed-sits, flats, bungalows and shared houses where a warden is at hand to assist with day-to-day problems, an accident or an emergency. There is usually a communal living area as well, often with meals provided and some social activities. Many sheltered schemes are run by the local authority, others by voluntary organizations, housing associations and private bodies, and accommodation can be rented or bought.

  Most sheltered accommodation caters only for older people who are mentally and physically active and would be unsuitable for those who are more dependent. The local authority housing or social services department, Citizens' Advice Bureau or Housing Advice Centre would be able to tell you what sheltered schemes there are in your area, and Age Concern have useful booklets on the subject.

- **Mobility and wheelchair housing**
  This is housing that has been specially adapted for those who are disabled or in a wheelchair. It is usually at ground-floor level with specially planned kitchen and bathroom layouts. There may be raised electric sockets (appliances that plug into sockets at skirting level that enable the old person to use the socket at a more convenient height, avoiding having to bend), ramps, wider passageways and other modifications so that disabled people can get around more easily. Some housing associations and private developers as well as local authorities are now building this type of accommodation, and you can find out if there is any locally by contacting the same sources mentioned above.

- **Residential homes**
  These provide accommodation plus communal dining room and lounge, and meals and domestic tasks are covered by the staff. Some will have private bed-sitting rooms where residents can take their furniture and some personal belongings; others have shared bedrooms. A

great many residential homes are run by the local authority social services department and voluntary organizations, but because of the general shortage and long waiting lists, an increasing number are opening that are private so that fees need to be paid. In cases of real need it is possible that the local authority or DHSS will help towards this cost, so contact your local social services department for information. A useful source of advice about residential homes are GRACE and Counsel and Care for the Elderly, but because standards vary, it is very important to look at a selection of homes before making a decision.

- **Nursing homes**
These are run by voluntary organizations and private individuals as well as by the local authority, but all should be registered with the district health authority. The homes provide full nursing care for infirm elderly people and must have fully qualified nursing staff on duty night and day. Again, because of a shortage of local authority and voluntary homes there are often waiting lists, but the DHSS may help towards the cost of private care. The social services department will have information.

- **Hospital or hospice**
There are still hospital beds available specializing in the care of infirm or seriously ill older people, but these tend to be short-term and if there is anyone at home able to do the caring, then they may well be discharged. Some hospitals will take a very disabled and dependant person for a few weeks to allow the carer to have a break, as will some residential and nursing homes. There are also a growing number of hospices that care for older terminally ill people in a sympathetic and understanding way. These can be the ideal solution to combining home and hospital care, allowing older people to go home during a good patch and then return to the hospice when necessary.

The organization Counsel and Care for the Elderly issues a helpful leaflet called *Accommodation for People Over Retiring Age*. Age Concern has published *Your Housing in Retirement* and *A Guide to Sheltered Housing* and The College of Health produces a booklet called *Homes for Elderly People* (for the addresses of these organizations, see pages 145 and 146.)

There are many other possibilities for the relatively independent older person. The Abbeyfield Society, for instance, runs family-sized houses for single elderly people in all parts of the country, and the National Association of Almshouses can give details of accommodation for local residents.

There are also associations catering for the needs of many people of foreign nationality who have settled in this country and many run homes for the elderly. Traditional culture and earlier memories become increasingly important as people become older and this can be a great comfort to them

One carer's mother who had come from Russia in the 1920s became so mentally confused that she needed full-time professional care. For a while she went to a small Polish home in London, and for the first time in many years was able to talk in Russian.

Choice for carers

Those taking on the task of caring for an elderly relative or friend should feel that they have some choice in the matter, too. Often it is a particular member of a family who becomes a carer, sometimes several times over. In one survey carried out by the Equal Opportunities Commission it was found that a high proportion of these are women who are already growing older themselves. There are some understandable reasons why this may be the case. Women are often more available than men because they are still frequently home-based. They tend to be older because this is when parents or partners need extra care and, on average, men become ill and die earlier than women. Women are also generally seen as the 'natural' carers with their traditional roles of wife, mother, and housekeeper, plus the conditioning of a society that still promotes these stereotyped ideas.

In many cases women are willing and happy to become carers, seeing it as simply another part of a loving relationship, but families and friends should never take this for granted, and nor should carers themselves. If they have strong feelings on the subject, these should be aired.

Judith Oliver, founder of the Association of Carers and a carer herself for many years, thinks it is most important that a relative or friend should be able to consider the question of becoming a carer calmly and objectively, without fear of guilt or blame.

'Some people find that they are caring for up to four relatives at a time', she says, 'The more they do it, the more they get asked. There are women with a whole trail of relatives to look after who can't get out of it because they already have a dependant. But it is most important to be able to decide whether you are the right person to do the job. The worst thing for both carer and cared for is if you are not, but go ahead out of a feeling of duty or guilt.

'You may not like a parent particularly, but be known to be by nature a rather caring person and also happen to be more available. Caring can be especially difficult in a marriage because it changes the relationship so much. It is no longer an equal partnership and the whole balance is changed.

'You only make a really good job of caring if you are repaying kindness. You should do it because you love them and want to help them. If not, you won't be doing any favours, and it is better instead to look for other ways.'

Sharing the task

Even when one person does take on the main bulk of caring, this should be seen as something to share among other relatives and friends. It is also most important that caring should be shared between men *and* women.

There are times when a dependant man might prefer the help of another male, such as when going to the toilet or being bathed. Just because a person is physically and mentally frail, it does not mean that he or she loses the need for privacy and dignity.

In purely practical ways men may have the extra physical strength to support, lift and carry than a woman; so, even if for various reasons men do not take on the role of main carer, they should still help regularly.

If there is a wider family or circle of friends available, they can take it in turns to give the carer a break, either on a day-today basis or during weekends and holidays. To have rest, in mind as well as body, is extremely important for carers, and makes the job much more enjoyable and successful during the remainder of the time.

Most carers I have talked to feel it is essential that arrangements like these should be made right at the beginning, with a combined plan drawn up and even agreed in writing. Otherwise it is so easy to let things slip and for the rest of the family to forget to play their part. The carer may then get too tired, downtrodden or hopeless to ask any more.

Even when caring for elderly people starts at home, there may come a time when the strain is too much and hospital, hospice or nursing home is the only answer. Again, many relatives and friends might fight against this, feeling they are somehow failing. Kathy Weir, the Family Welfare Association counsellor, explains:

> 'So many carers love and do their best for those they look after. It's hard for them to admit they can't go on, but if the carer feels it is intolerable, then it *is* intolerable. It's so easy to think you are being weak and inadequate, and that if only you could pull yourself together and be stronger then you'd be able to do it.
>
> 'One member of our support group had to have a short stay in hospital, which meant that her elderly aunt had to go into hospital and eventually into a home. The group has helped this carer accept her dilemma. She wants to carry on looking after her aunt to give her peace and dignity in her last years, but the breakdown in her own health has forced her to consider the quality of her own life. But because you stop caring *for* someone, it doesn't mean you stop caring *about* them.'

Help from outside

The other major step to take when planning the future care of an ageing person is to find out exactly what services do exist for carers in your particular area. 'It's no good waiting for offers because you will be left to do it on your own', says Judith Oliver. 'Get your support system round you at the beginning, because you can always off-load later. If you soldier on without help and then ask, it will be much more difficult to get what you need.'

You may be lucky and live in a place where services are very good, or you may find there is very little. This should also influence any decisions about where the care should take place.

The following are the main sources of information:

- **General practitioners**

  Good GPs should be in touch with the local support network and may already be familiar with your particular situation. They should be key people in ensuring carers get, or are referred to, the medical and social services listed here, but some GPs are more knowledgable than others and it may be necessary to make further independent enquiries.

- **Social services department**

  The social services department of the local authority is the gateway to many services, including home helps (or domiciliary helps as they may be called), meals on wheels, transport, and day and respite centres for older people. Some have social workers specializing in the care of the elderly who will know what services are available and suitable. Most have community occupational therapists who can visit the home and advise on aids and adaptations, grants and therapy for overcoming some handicaps.

- **District health authority**

  The health authority (often called the community health authority) can advise on local community nursing services. These should include district or community nurses who can help with practical nursing in the home, a health visitor who may specialize in the care of older people, a community physiotherapist who can visit you in your home and advise on mobility problems and give exercise. Some areas now have a community psychiatric nurse who can offer guidance to those carers who look after older people suffering from mental illness and confusion. The health authority should also be able to advise on hospital, nursing home and hospice care.

- **Hospital**

  If an older person has been discharged from hospital to

home, then the hospital can be a very useful source of information and practical support. The geriatric specialist could recommend and even arrange suitable support, such as community nursing, physiotherapy, occupational therapy and speech therapy. Some hospitals now have continence advisers and there should also be a hospital social worker, who is another important source of knowledge about local facilities and financial help, in the form of welfare benefits and grants.

● **DHSS**
There is a range of welfare benefits from the Department of Health and Social Security to help both the carer and the cared-for financially. These include Attendance Allowance, Invalid Care Allowance, Income Support, Mobility Allowance and the Social Fund. Details about these, and other financial support, are in Chapters 3 and 7.

Voluntary organizations

As will be seen throughout this book, voluntary organizations are a vital source of support for carers and their dependants. In spite of the name, these are not necessarily staffed by volunteers but employ salaried, professional people as organizers and workers. They are independent of the local authority services and are funded from many sources, though this will often include the Department of Health and Social Security and local councils.

Voluntary organizations offer a huge range of services for carers, both at a national and local level, including care attendants, social and luncheon clubs and day centres for older people, transport, counselling, support groups and a wide range of helpful publications. Some, like the Carers National Association, offer support on every aspect of caring. Some, like the Chest, Heart and Stroke Association and the Parkinson's Disease Society offer help for those with a particular disability. Some, like the Red Cross can provide nursing aids and training, and some like Crossroads provide care attendants who can come in to the home and give skilled help and a break for the carer.

Many voluntary organizations are locally-based, self-help, neighbourhood, community and church schemes, but many others have a national central office that can provide information and details of publications and, usually, details of a local branch of the organization.

Addresses of the national organizations are listed in our last section. To find out what they may offer in your area, ask head offices for addresses of local branches and contacts. Your local reference library should have a list of helping organizations, and there may also be a Volunteer Bureau, Community Health Council or central agency for voluntary organizations in the area the staff of which can advise you. (For further information on all types of services for carers, see Chapters 7 and 8.)

Understanding the changes

Where an elderly person is looked after will mostly depend on who takes on the main caring role. If this is a partner, friend or single relative then they may remain in their own homes. If the carer already has another family, then older people will often move in with them. Either way there are likely to be stresses and strains of one sort or another as everyone adjusts to the new situation. So another very important part of preparing to care for an older person is to be ready for the various changes that growing older can bring.

Not everyone, of course, does change with age. Some will feel more frail than others, but this may not necessarily be because they are older. Circumstances unconnected with age such as character, personality, health, finances and life experiences will all have their effects. Even so, there do seem to be some shared characteristics among older people and most especially those who are ill. Anxiety, lack of confidence in themselves, fear of the future, irritability, demands for reassurance are commonly and understandably found. The trouble for many carers is that they feel they are the *cause* of such responses rather than that these are existing quite independently in the other person. By understanding a little more about the psychology of ageing they realise this is the case, and there are plenty of examples of this. In one study of carers the story is told of a woman who struggled on for months blaming herself for her mother's shouting and screaming fits. Then one day it was confirmed that her mother was mentally unstable and from that day the carer was able to come to terms with her mother's irrational behaviour. In my own case, I remember when my mother was given only three months to live I had a romantic vision of making this time memorable with treats and trips. In reality she was irritable and depressed in a way she had never been before. Though no one explained it at the time, I now know it was part of her illness and she had to be supported as gently and optimistically as possible through her difficulties.

A very helpful book to read is *Family Care of Old People* by Tim Dartington (Souvenir Press, 1980). In one passage on the mental processes of ageing he points out how much of what appears 'difficult' to deal with in older people is simply their own way of keeping their sense of independence and individuality against all odds. Increased dependence, he explains, brings on an increased urgency to keep one's own sense of worth. In trying to continue to be individuals, older people can be obstinate, apparently putting their needs before others. They can withdraw from the world and become angry and aggressive. Sometimes they may give up altogether and there can be dramatic changes in behaviour: they no longer bother to eat or dress properly, they may become dirty and purposely wet or soil themselves, but given care and understanding they can be encouraged to feel they *do* matter. Even though they are older and may have lost so much of what they once had, such as a partner, good health, a job and income, they are still people of worth in their own right.

A sense of loss

For many carers it is a sense of loss of the older person as he or she used to be that is the saddest aspect to come to terms with. Even though the relative or friend is still there, they feel bereaved. Says one husband of his wife:

> 'She's not getting any better, that's for sure. I love her dearly, but she is not the person she was. My GP doles out pills. Pills for her and pills for me. We can't put the clock back, but what I regret most is not having the quiet times with her. We've always shared our feelings, both happy and sad, and we need to do that more now than ever before.'

Says a wife about her husband:

> 'It's a strain from morning till night. He's become so selfish. I tell him he can't have everything he wants when he wants it, like a spoiled child, and then I bite my tongue. But it does make me feel his personality has totally changed – it's like living with a stranger.'

The loss in such cases is not just of the person, but of the relationship. A husband and wife may be together, but they are no longer sharing the sexual, emotional or intellectual life they once had. A mother and daughter may be in the same house, but there is no trace of the closeness they used to feel.

One counsellor who has worked a great deal with carers feels that the process of adjustment to these changes is very much like that of mourning during bereavement. First comes a lack of belief and acceptance, with the carer constantly looking for signs of recovery and a complete return to how things were. Sometimes with improved health this may happen, but if it doesn't then there may be deep sadness and a feeling of apathy. There may also be a period of anger and despair as the carer has to come to terms with reality. Finally can come adjustment, and with that a certain peace and even enjoyment. At least, relatives or friends may think, I still have them with me; at least there is still the chance to love and care for them in the best way possible, even if there are limitations.

> 'Every moment can become very precious. Pleasure can be found in very simple things. I remember one husband who told me of his pride in how he was learning to manage.
>
> 'He had been very dependent on his wife for looking after the home and, as he said, "all the wifely things." Now he actually enjoyed picking the flowers and arranging them, not just for her, but for both of them.'

Switching roles

A reversal of roles is another very common experience for carers: children may have to become parent figures, and parents, in many cases, become like children; husbands take over the role of housewives and wives take on all sorts of jobs that once they left to their husbands. As has been pointed out in a study of these caring problems entitled *Family Care of the Handicapped Elderly: Who Pays?*, some people are able to accept this change in roles instinctively and there are no problems, while others never quite manage to cope with the change, roles remain unclear and unsatisfactory and no one, young or old, is happy.

The book quotes the example of a married couple who moved in with the wife's father to look after him when he had a stroke. Everyone in the household was very conscious of the home being the father's, and the couple continued to feel like visitors. The daughter, even after cooking in the kitchen for 13 years, still considered it to be her father's and was worried about rearranging things. He did not like her going out or bringing friends in because he found this too disruptive.

One carer who wrote to me was a loving and conscientious daughter who looked after her mother for many years. Nevertheless she found it very hard to cope with her mother's refusal to accept that now she was the one who needed looking after and not the other way round:

> 'My mother had been a nursing sister and was very attractive and charming and used to being a leader. I was very fond of her indeed, but after developing heart trouble at 74 she changed completely.
>
> 'Nothing was right for her and the jealousy of a younger woman – even a daughter – doing what she used to do was unbelievable. She had always been so active and energetic and she loathed having to be looked after.'

In another case the relationship of a 58-year-old daughter with her father returned almost completely to the days when she was a young child. 'My father was very much the disciplinarian and I was not allowed to do as I liked.'

Other types of conflict can involve the wider family – husbands may resent the amount of time and affection that a wife is giving to her parents, children may resent the presence of the older person, particularly if this interferes with their freedom or makes it difficult when friends are around.

Many people need to work through a great deal of past conflict with older people such as their parents before they can challenge and come to terms with these changes in their lives. Complex emotions of guilt and anger confused with love and tenderness will be present. These feelings have to be understood, accepted and revised to fit the new reality of a frail, elderly person who is dependent upon us.

Counselling (when a trained person helps you look at your life and your relationship and see how these could work better) can be very beneficial, so can assertiveness training, which encourages you to realize your true worth and stand up for your own needs. Both are discussed in more detail in later chapters, but to understand the feelings of older people and their losses as well as your own will also go a long way to easing many potential problems.

Smoothing the way

Here are a few tips from other carers that they have found helpful when handling an older person who has become unreasonable and difficult:

- 'If you do have disagreements, try and reserve them for issues that really matter. If you give in over smaller matters you are more likely to remain calm and more likely to win the argument about important things.'
- 'Be definite and clear when discussing arrangements. If you introduce a whole series of probabilities and uncertainties you will almost certainly find your message has been misunderstood. Anxiety about such matters will loom large for someone who has the whole day to reflect.'
- 'If you sense an older person is becoming over pre-occupied with a certain problem or discussion, a quick change of subject or scene can spare a good deal of needless upset.'

- 'A sense of humour is a great boon. Rather than fretting and becoming tearful over a slow progression to the bathroom, try to find a humorous comment which relieves tension.'

- 'Be prepared for unexpected interludes. Elderly people have their own rhythms and may enrich your day quite unexpectedly by some recollections or some memories which they want to share while you want to get on with the washing up. But if you can, sit and listen, as such times can bring you both unexpected riches.'

CHAPTER 3
Some practical arrangements

'From my own experience caring for my mother a simple gadget, like a helping hand which can pick things up from the floor or a trolley used as a walking aid, enables the older person to be as independent as possible'

'First we had to rearrange the house to allow a bed to be brought downstairs as the stairs were too steep. This meant giving up our dining room, leaving one room for sitting, eating and so on'

Organizing the accommodation

Much that can be done to make life easier for the carer as well as the older person is practical. A home that is safe, comfortable and well organized can cut down on many potential problem areas before they even arise. A lot will depend, of course, on where home is. If you are living in the older person's house or calling in to look after a relative or friend on a daily basis, then it may be difficult to make suggestions and changes. Even in your own home you may be limited by the size of the house, the number of other family members living there or lack of money.

If it's possible for the older person to have a bed-sitting room on the ground floor with a nearby toilet and bathroom, this is the ideal arrangement. Even if an older person is able to get up and down stairs at first, increasing age or disability may later make this difficult, if not impossible.

Some are luckier than others. One carer I talked to described how, as part of a long-term plan for the future, she, her husband and her mother-in-law sold their two homes to

buy one large one. They now share this, with the addition of a
new baby daughter.

'We were fortunate because the house is big enough for my
mother-in-law to have two rooms to herself, with her own
small kitchen and bathroom all on the same level. Though she
has an arthritic hip, she is able to get around and look after
herself as much as possible.

'After a fall she was frightened to live alone, and this gives her company and our care when necessary, but also independence. If and when the time comes for her to need more help, she will still have space for privacy – and so will we.'

Buying or renting a home together can have its difficulties, however, and in Chapter 7 there is advice on drawing up a legal contract. Age Concern has a helpful booklet called *Sharing Your Home*.

Typical for many carers is the situation experienced by Joyce, a single woman living with her parents who gave up her job to look after her mother full-time after her father died. Her mother also had arthritis, and a double hip operation was only partially successful.

'From that time until she died she could only move her leg by leaning with her hands on two sticks or a walking frame. Then mother had a slight fall which unnerved her and from that time she seemed to go downhill.

'First we had to rearrange the house to allow a bed to be brought downstairs as the stairs were too steep. This meant giving up our dining room, leaving one room for sitting, eating, etc. The new bedroom also became my mother's toilet room as we had no toilet downstairs.

'I was advised to get in touch with the local social services, whom I must say were very good and supplied us free a pole for the bed to help mother to help herself into bed, and also a new commode of a better height and an armchair.

'Also in the last two years of her life we had to change doctors and a younger more caring one came who was much more understanding and got in the district nurses. They were a marvellous bunch of people who brought me, free, everything I could possibly need for mother's convenience and comfort.'

Planning the space

If space is very limited, it may be necessary for relations and friends to think very seriously about whether it is advisable to look after someone at home. The natural stresses can be made worse by a confined situation, and it is important that the

carer as well as the cared for have room to be on their
own sometimes.

This is all part of the important human need to remain an
individual as well as a friend, companion and partner. To
retain some sense of our own identity and a feeling that *our*
needs matter too, we all need to be alone as well as together.
This is even more true when one person's life revolves
around caring for another. This is why, whatever the size of
the home, the older person should have a bedroom of his or
her own which can double as a sitting room by day. The
following extras are also helpful:

● **A sofa bed**
  Unless the older person is bed-ridden, a bed which folds
  into a settee is a good investment. This makes the room
  look less like a bedroom during the day and means that
  there is a base from which he or she can entertain family
  and friends.

● **Separate TV**
  This adds to the feeling of independence, and means that
  there will be fewer clashes over which programmes to
  watch, especially when there is a large family of mixed
  generations to cater for. TV rental companies may have
  special rental rates, and the Wireless for the Bedridden
  Society is an organization that provides radios and TVs to
  those in need.

● **Tea-making equipment**
  If an older person is physically or mentally very frail this
  might be a danger, but, if possible, provide an electric ket-
  tle plus a small store of provisions, china and cutlery so that
  snacks can be prepared independently of the family. This
  increases feelings of privacy and self-esteem.

● **Ornaments**
  Wherever possible include older people's own treasured
  pieces of furniture, ornaments, photographs and so on.
  One part of the house is then theirs, full of their own particular memories, and this increases security and feelings
  of well-being.

● **Separate telephone**
  It may be possible for older people to have their own

telephone. For the carer this is an essential means of contact with the outside world; but it can be equally helpful to the cared for, keeping them in touch with friends and other members of the family. Ask the social services department whether they can help towards the cost of installation or rent.

● **Washbasin**

A washbasin in the room is nice for older people, especially if they have difficulty in getting around. It also saves on queues to the bathroom, a frequent source of tension when a family is sharing!

Aids and adaptations

It's also important when sorting out accommodation to find out about the various adaptations that can be made to the house, the aids that are available and the grants paid to help towards travel costs.

Under the Chronically Sick and Disabled Person's Act, 1970, a local authority should assess your ability to pay for adaptations to the house, but grants vary in different areas. To find out what the situation is where you live, contact both the social services and housing departments.

It is also a good idea to talk to the GP and an occupational therapist who can advise on the sort of aids most helpful to

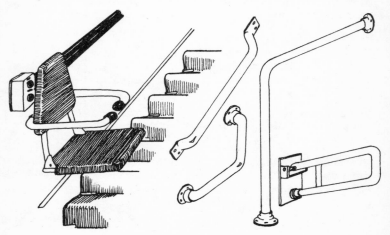

the particular disabilities of the person being looked after. For instance, if space allows, it may be possible to install a toilet or shower on the ground floor or to add a lift or handrails to the stairs. Handrails can also be fixed in the bathroom or hall and in other rooms.

If the older person is in a wheelchair then special ramps can be built and doors widened. A raised toilet seat (a fitting that is attached to the existing seat that raises the height of the toilet seat to make it easier for the older person to get on and off), various bath aids or special taps on the washbasins and kitchen sink that are pulled instead of twisted can make a great deal of difference to the independence of older people and carers.

The Disabled Living Foundation (DLF) and the Royal Association for Disability and Rehabilitation (RADAR) are both excellent sources of information on what aids and adaptations are available and how to get them. There are also Regional Aids Centres where equipment can be demonstrated and where carers can get specialist advice on a wide range of disabilities. Beware, though, as with everything else, there can be pitfalls. One carer who bought a large house with her husband when his ailing parents came to live with them, had a downstairs shower room installed thinking they qualified for a 90 per cent grant, only to discover that, because the house did not belong to the parents, they only qualified for a 50 per cent grant. The DHSS eventually agreed to make up the difference – but over two years later the family were still waiting for the money.

The answer is, always ask what differences exist when grants are for people living in their own accommodation as opposed to those living with someone else. This can make a difference to everything that is on offer, from whether you are eligible for a home help to types of grants and benefits. So check the small print every time.

Safety first

Safety in the home is another important consideration. As people grow older they can be less steady on their feet, hearing and sight become less acute and there may be a tendency to dizziness and loss of balance. So, without completely rearranging the house, it is a good idea to check each room through from the safety angle, taking certain precautions that may prevent accidents such as falls and burns.

The Royal Society for the Prevention of Accidents (RoSPA) has a useful booklet giving advice on how to make the home generally safer for older people and this contains a checklist of points to look for. Here are some important areas:

- Low tables, stools, children's toys and general household clutter in every room can all be a hazard. A tidy house with not too many knick knacks means that there are fewer things to trip over or knock into.
- Loose mats or staircarpets, rucked up rugs and highly polished floors are all potential dangers. Handrails help, but take a good look to see that flooring is secure and unslippery.
- The same applies in garden or patio. Uneven, cracked paths and paving are the cause of many falls. Handrails will help, and outline any awkward steps in white.
- Trailing flexes need tucking away. If you have an open fire then a fireguard is essential, and electric fires need to be the type that cannot be knocked over. Paraffin heaters should also be avoided.
- Good lighting is another necessity for older people. Have a switch inside the front door and at top and bottom of stairs, plus a bedside light in case he or she want to get up in the night.
- Burns and scalds are a peril for older people. Have saucepans with small handles if possible, or turn longer handles inwards so that that don't stick out from the cooker. Safety devices for gas taps can be supplied by the Gas Board.
- Medicines should be clearly labelled and stored in a cool, dry place. Don't keep sleeping pills by an older person's bed in case an extra dose is taken by mistake (more about medicines on pages 76–78.)

It pays to take care like this because accidents and injury are not only hard for the older person to cope with, but will also mean more difficulties for carers. The fewer hazards there are around the house, the more independent you can all be.

Keeping warm

Older people are affected by the cold more than younger ones, and this is particularly so when they are disabled in some way and therefore less active. They will need extra heating in the home, and this can be difficult when finances are stretched already. Another problem is that older people can become very cold without realizing it. The body has its own thermostat and in younger people this mechanism protects vital organs and the brain by diverting the blood away from the surface of the skin, reducing heat loss to a minimum. In some older people their thermostat fails to function correctly and so heat will be lost from the body and the vital organs cool to dangerously low temperatures, well below the normal range. This is called hypothermia and can be fatal.

A healthy diet keeps cold at bay. This should be well-balanced with meat, fish, eggs, cheese, vegetables, potatoes, bread and fresh fruit included. A hot cereal like porridge is a good start to the day, and as many as nine hot drinks daily during colder weather are recommended to help maintain a warm body temperature.

Several layers of clothing are better than one thick one and special thermal underwear and outerwear insulates against the cold. It's also important to keep extremities warm with socks, gloves and even a nightcap when temperatures drop very low. As much as 20 per cent of the body's warmth can be lost through the scalp alone if it is left uncovered.

When it comes to actually heating the home, background warmth with night storage heaters is an economical method and those on very low incomes may also qualify for special heating allowances during very severe weather, so check whether you are eligible with the DHSS. A lot of advice and help is available on making the most of heat in the home but here are a few tips. Insulating the loft and lagging the hot water tanks come high on the list, and there are grants available to help towards the cost of having this done. Heavy curtains at the windows and over the front door, draught excluders for doors and letterboxes, shelves above radiators and silver foil behind them to reflect heat back into the room and filling or covering gaps between floor boards, will all minimize heat loss. For further information, take a look at *Warmth in Winter* from Age Concern and *Ways to Keep Warm This Winter* from Help the Aged. Both are very useful publications packed with money-saving tips. Help the Aged also produce a special factsheet called *Insulating Your Home* that includes information on grants.

Keeping fit

There are many things that can be done to ensure that older people stay fit and in control of their own lives for as long as possible. Dr Muir Gray is a community physician who has worked for a number of years with older people and those who care for them, and he firmly believes in encouraging independence and activity as a way of keeping fit. In one Help the Aged report he points out that:

'Fitness can best be defined as the ability of the body to respond to challenge without upset. At the age of 20 it will decide whether you can climb a mountain or swim a length. At the age of 80 how fit you are determines whether or not you can climb a flight of stairs or walk to the shops.

'Fitness is also to do with keeping mind and body active. Being "grown-up" in our society is usually associated with being fairly inactive. Older people are much less able to cope with immobility, yet socially 10-year olds go out and play football while 40-year-olds sit and drink coffee.

'It's also to do with attitudes – both the beliefs of older people about themselves and the beliefs of other people about them. Some older people feel that the body can wear away with use. Yet those who remain active are far more likely to be healthy.'

Experience has shown Dr Gray that negative attitudes are often reinforced by those around. Professionals, in particular, may see so many disabled people in the course of their work that they start thinking *all* elderly people are disabled. As Dr Muir Gray says:

> 'An over-protective attitude and an underestimation of their capabilities and potential still prevails. The general reaction of the public to an older person struggling to do something is: "You sit there and I will do it for you", but what I would see here is a loss of fitness because one of the important aspects of fitness is self-care.'

He recognizes the difficult tightrope that both professional and home carers walk between helping and actually '*dis*abling' older people. Most of us are acting out of kindness and concern when we do things for them, and many may feel there is simply no choice, but some carers are surprised to see what relatives and friends are capable of in differing circumstances. One wife could not believe how much her husband achieved at his day centre compared with when he was at home with her:

> 'After my husband's stroke he would ask me to do everything – from putting on his slippers in the morning to holding his cup when he drank his tea and cutting up his food and giving it to him on a fork, yet at the day centre they told me he often walked unaided to the toilet and fed himself quite well. He was slow and he would grumble, but he did it. I think I had been frightened of pushing him in case it damaged him, but far from this being so we found the more he did, the more he could achieve.'

This carer, like many others, did everything for him because she saw this as part of loving and looking after him. It's also very easy to be manipulated into this position and do things for someone thinking it is a necessity when actually they are feeling lazy and unmotivated. At the same time, however, recognizing the limits is important. Creating constant battles by pushing older people well beyond their capabilities only causes unnecessary upsets and distress for all concerned; but to gently, firmly and, with the advice of the professionals involved, encourage older people to do as much as possible for themselves can reap benefits for everyone.

Keeping active

Dr Muir Gray believes there are many ways in which the health services can help older people remain more active, particularly those still able to live in their own homes. Meals on Wheels, for instance, perform a service that is essential for many, but he points out too that for some elderly people cooking their own lunch, however long this takes, is good physiotherapy and occupational therapy, and without it they spend a lot of time simply sitting around.

In the Help the Aged report Dr Muir Gray notes that 'Similarly, home helps can be essential, but it is much cheaper for the health authorities and much easier for home helps to nip down to the shops themselves and much more difficult and time-consuming to walk there with the elderly person.'

Providing transport so that older people can continue to attend over-sixties clubs, luncheon clubs and day centres can also be vital in encouraging them to keep active and in touch with the world outside. Through organizations like Pensioner's Link and Age Concern some over-sixties have for the first time in their lives become active campaigners for better rights, particularly where pensions and other benefits are concerned. Far from settling back into rocking chairs, they have discovered new talents in themselves.

Some over-sixty clubs concentrate on aspects of self-help health, with talks on nutrition, health care, exercise and relaxation. Others provide entertainment, bingo, dancing and creative activities. Many older people get a great deal of enjoyment and comfort from life-history projects that explore their past through photographs, mementoes and memories. Such groups are springing up in all parts of the country now, and have the added advantage that they include every age group, young as well as old. This is important because not all older people want to mix exclusively with others of the same age. To discover interests and then search out clubs and groups that will foster and encourage these can be a better idea.

Generally speaking much more imagination is used now in providing stimulating activities, even within groups catering purely for older people. This can come as quite a surprise.

One carer reports how when he tried to take his wife to the local day centre, she refused to go in: 'When we walked through the door she smelt cooking and said "I'm not staying here, I'm coming home. They're all old ladies and men. I don't want to go somewhere making dolls and doing knitting". Had she stayed, she would probably have found a great deal more than she imagined, from art to cookery and gardening. Many centres now work at encouraging older people to widen their interests rather than narrow them down, and to overcome disabilities with new activities.

All this may seem to be aimed at the elderly person alone, but there is no doubt that carers benefit as well. Not only will these outside activities give *them* more time to pursue their own interests, but it will keep their dependant happier and healthier when they are together.

Home entertainments

When illness or disablement makes older people unable or unwilling to go out, then this creates new problems for carers as well as the cared for. In some areas local authority home visiting schemes exist. For instance, there may be a craft instructor who can come in and work with the older person. The social services department or adult education department may be able to advise on this.

In Norfolk there is an organization called Extend that offers advice on exercises for older people to do in the home and even in a wheelchair. These encourage improved posture, co-ordination and fitness through music and movement (for their address, see page 149.) To give you an idea of the kind of exercises that are good for inactive elderly people, reproduced overleaf are exercises put together by a gymnast for the Leicestershire Health Education Unit. Even though the movements are minimal, done regularly each day they keep muscles stronger and joints more supple. Occupational therapists and physiotherapists from social services and community health departments may also be able to advise on suitable activities and interests for the homebound. Two useful publications recommended in our Further Reading section

Exercises for the inactive elderly

For the fingers and wrists
Stretch your fingers apart and then close them back together again, either both hands at once or alternately
Wiggle your fingers up and down, as if you were playing a piano
Shake your wrists

For the arms
Touch your shoulders with your hands and then lift your hands up off your shoulders, stretching your arms out to your sides
Lift your arms, one at a time, up into the air
Touch your right elbow with you left hand, then touch your left elbow with your right hand and repeat
Clap your hands
Clap your hands up in the air
Clasp your hands together, move them in towards your chest and then stretch them straight out in front of you, still clasped together
Clasp your hands together and stretch them up and down
With your arms bent at the elbows, in front of your chest, rotate your arms in small circles

For the shoulders
With your hands placed on your shoulders, shrug your shoulders then hunch them forwards and stretch them back, using your elbows to help you
Shrug your shoulders, together, up and down
Shrug one shoulder then the other, up and down
With your hands linked together, move your arms across your chest, as if you were rocking a baby
With your arms and hands outstretched, turn the palms of your hands to face up and then down

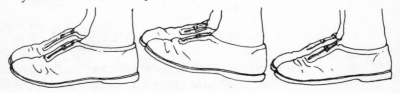

For the feet and ankles

Sitting in a chair or on the edge of your bed with your feet together, flat on the floor, move them in small circles clockwise and then anticlockwise, keeping your feet together and on the floor

In the same position as the last exercise, keep your heels on the floor and lift your toes up then down.

For the abdomen

Start with your hands just resting on your thighs. Reach forwards and grasp your knees, then return your hands to your thighs

With your hands clasped together, swing them from side to side

Clap your hands, first to one side and then to the other

Lean forward and clap your hands down by your knees

With your hands together, touch your chest, then touch your lower leg and then move back to your waist

For the legs

Tap your feet on the floor, up and down

If possible sit on a table or chair so that your feet do not quite touch the floor and then gently swing your feet forwards and backwards

Sitting with your legs straight out in front of you, lift your left knee, bringing your left foot as close to your right knee as you can manage without straining and then reverse, repeating the exercise with your right leg

Sitting in a chiar, raise your knees alternately

These exercises, compiled by a gymnast at Leicester General Hospital, are recommended by the Leicester Health Education Unit and should be practised sitting down. They can be made more fun when set to music with a pronounced beat, and older people should be encouraged to do what they can *without* overstraining.

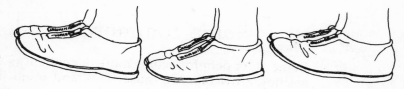

(see page 157) also give lots of ideas for creative things to do at home as well as in clubs.

One carer stresses the importance of friends for both carer *and* the older person. After looking after her mother for many years, she remembers with gratitude those who called spontaneously, ready to 'take you as you are':

> 'Thanks to those would would stay for short periods and sit with the patient, so identifying with them and not just looking at them as if remote, who would listen and who would talk about things and people familiar to the older person like family and weather, and be cheerful, bringing in a taste of the outside world.
>
> 'They didn't have to do a lot, overwhelming the patient, but little things like reading to them, playing with them, doing up a button, which meant a lot but did not involve fussing – just treating them as normal!
>
> 'Sometimes visits from such friends would (unknown to them) draw together a few broken strands in the family relationships, cover up a few niggling hurts and interactions which are inevitable in a closely knit situation. Such visits would be the making of the day, however brief.'

Keeping healthy

There are other important ways of helping older people stay healthy, some of which are easily overlooked but can make a great difference to the quality of their lives as well as the lives of carers. Top of the list are the following:

- **Dental care**
  Teeth can cause a lot of problems and six-monthly check-ups are as important for older people as younger. These will alert the dentist to softening gums, decay, infection, loose teeth or ill-fitting dentures, all of which can cause discomfort and make eating difficult. The check-up, treatment for bleeding and denture repairs are free to pensioners under the NHS. If you do not have an NHS dentist, contact the dental officer through the district or community health authority. It may also be possible to arrange a home visit from a dentist.

Daily diet

You will be following a health diet, supplying you with all the nutrients, minerals and vitamins you need, if it includes daily:

- 285–570ml/½–1pint milk – taken as drinks, with cereals, in milk puddings, custard or as yogurt
- 1 egg – boiled, poached, scrambled, or beaten into milk
- 30g/1oz cheese or 55–85g/2–3oz meat, fish or poultry. Try to eat liver or kidney once a week and similarly sardines, kippers, mackerel, herring or other fish
- 2–3 slices of bread – wholemeal bread is better than white or brown bread as the fibre content will help prevent constipation
- two helpings of vegetables, one of which can be potato (jacket potatoes retain more of their goodness than boiled or creamed potatoes)
- one helping of fruit, particularly oranges, or a glass of natural fruit juice

  Eating smaller, more frequent meals is better than having one big meal each day and do remember to drink plenty of fluids

● Nutrition

Older people frequently have smaller appetites – especially when unwell, or when there is difficulty with swallowing and chewing – but it is still vitally important that they should eat a balanced diet to remain healthy. A nutritious diet keeps hypothermia at bay and mind and body in better working order. Folic acid is often deficient in older people and there may be a low intake of vitamins, protein and iron. Opposite is a recommended daily intake that includes essential foods. Small, frequent meals are better than one big one, and the daily diet should include plenty of fluids. Cutting back on drinks doesn't improve incontinence and can actually do harm to the older person's general health (more about this on page 76.) Information on nutrition generally and on special diets in particular are available from many sources, including Community Health Education Units, the Nutrition Education Service, dieticians at local hospitals and organizations dealing with specific illnesses, such as the British Diabetic Association.

● **Foot care**

Feet can be another unsuspected but disabling source of trouble as people grow older. Bunions, ingrowing toenails, hard skin, callouses and corns can cause pain and discomfort and difficulty in getting about. Under the NHS everyone on a pension can have free check-ups through the local community chiropody service. There may be a local clinic, mobile caravan or home visitor. Because of long waiting lists some people resort to private treatment and qualified chiropodists are listed in the Yellow Pages with SRCh after their names. Check how much treatment costs before booking, and those on a low income may be able to get financial help.

Eyes and ears also need regular check-ups to make sure that they are working efficiently, too (more about this on pages 88 and 90.)

Organizing a routine

Carers who have shared their homes for some time with older people all say how essential it is to lay down certain ground rules for living so that everyday life has a reasonably predictable structure and routine. Not only does this help the dependant person feel more secure and comfortable; it also helps ease some of the conflicts that can arise within families, especially if there is a wide age range under the same roof, including children and teenagers.

Small changes can make a great difference. For instance, a common cause of friction on both sides can be the playing of loud records, radios or musical instruments. To keep this to certain times of the day and/or invest in headphones so that the noise doesn't disturb older people, keeps everyone happy.

Having friends round can be another problem, but if the older generation have their own rooms as already suggested, and younger ones turn their bedrooms into bed-sits too, there are separate as well as communal spaces to live in and so conflict can be avoided. Here are a few more suggestions from carers:

- **Household chores**
  'Try and find ways older people can help you. The psychological benefits are considerable: they feel they are making a contribution; you feel tasks are being shared. If they are reasonably active and mentally stable they may be able to look after their own rooms, help with washing up and so on. But quite simple things, like going to the post office or bringing in the milk can become part of a meaningful routine for older people and save time for you.'

- **Sharing bills**
  'Discuss finance openly, and work out how bills are to be paid, small as well as large. Working out a weekly instalment system may help on regular outgoings, while more individual expenses such as newspapers and telephone calls can be paid as they arise. Managing on a low income makes careful budgeting even more necessary and it's important to top up with the Social Security benefits that are available.' (More details about finance are given in Chapter 7.)

- **Daily routine**
  'When there is a larger family to consider, it's very important to keep time to be with partner and children. I used to have lunch with my mother, then reserve the evenings for the rest of the family. She would have her evening snack in her room while we had supper and was quite happy with

the arrangement because it was an expected part of our daily routine. Weekends we all had together and any special celebrations such as birthdays and anniversaries.'

● **Holiday breaks**
'Right from the start make an arrangement about regular and separate holidays and breaks. Other relatives may agree to have older people to stay at certain times of the year or for so many weekends a month. Make definite arrangements and stick to them so that the older person knows what to expect.

Health of the carer

There is a loud PS to this chapter. Although much has been said so far about the health of the older person, it cannot be stressed often enough that it is just as important for carers to look after themselves. Too many neglect their own health in the interests of a relative or friend. If there is a shortage of money, then they are likely to spend what there is on the other person and neglect themselves. Diet is a typical example of this. With limited resources and time, they will use their energy to prepare tempting dishes for the older person and get by on snacks themselves. All the nutritional advice given here applies to you, carers, as well. Looking after someone else is an exhausting and demanding task and carers need good food for energy and strength. Sleep is vital, too, but nights are often disturbed when living with and looking after older people. It's therefore essential to find time during the day to catch up on lost rest. Don't see this as an indulgence, it's a necessity. The carers' health is important, not just for your own sakes but also for the sake of the people being looked after.

The next chapters explore in more detail the effects that physical and mental ill health can have not just on the older person but on the carer.

CHAPTER 4
Dealing with disability

'Relations and those others who have been close to patients can offer invaluable advice, guidance and clues to staff to assist in diagnosing patient's problems.'

'She is doubly incontinent. I have to wash on average 12–16 sheets and 6–7 nightdresses every 24 hours.'

A good diagnosis

The physical strains a carer will have to cope with and the symptoms of the cared for will naturally vary according to each particular disability or illness. That is why it is essential to get a good medical diagnosis of anything that is wrong, however old a dependant person is. Aches, pains, stiffness, rashes and all sorts of other symptoms are too often put down to ageing and then ignored, when an accurate diagnosis might mean something could be done to alleviate the problem.

The improvements in medical care during the last century mean that a lot more people are living for longer than ever before, but it doesn't mean that, once elderly, there is little that can be done to improve their health. Dr Muir Gray, the community physician, thinks that too many older people and those who care for them accept ill health because they are told to by professionals:

'They do not have enough sense of their right to good health and care. Some older people do believe that the problems they have are due to old age. They feel they cannot be treated because, well, "What do you expect at my age?", but often a

person thinks like this because a doctor has said, "What do
you expect at your age?" '

He also thinks that older people have lower expectations than
younger people because they have known hard times in the
past and have been disappointed by unfulfilled promises.

Another consultant working with older people strongly
believes that illness of the elderly should not be seen in a
negative way, as inevitable, but as a positive medical
challenge. What many regard as sad but unavoidable signs of
growing old he sees as symptoms which can be treated, if
only they are recognized. He points out incontinence as a
typical example. Older people and their carers often put up
with this condition for years, assuming it to be a part of growing older, but in this consultant's view many sufferers can be
cured and most can improve with the right course of action.
So it is important for older people and carers to insist that
signs of ill health are taken seriously and diagnosed properly.
If a GP is not helpful then all patients have the right to ask for
a second, even third, specialist opinion if they want it.

Doctors are often held too much in awe. We accept their
opinions because we don't like to argue and hope they know
best. This isn't always the case, and in the limited experience
of my family alone I know of frequent misdiagnosis or dis-
missal of symptoms, which has led to much more serious illness. In the case of my mother, the early signs of bowel cancer
were put down to indigestion until we insisted on an X-ray
and a tumour was discovered. My father was eventually
diagnosed as having cancer of the bone, which was initially
explained away as lumbago and old age. To insist on accurate
diagnosis can often lead to new and successful forms of treatment that alleviate an ill or disabled person's discomforts, or
even cure them completely. If caught early enough, many
potentially serious and even fatal conditions need not
develop at all.

Some common disorders

Some older people become more dependent and less mobile
as they grow older because body and mind have slowed

down and become generally less efficient in their working, but there are also specific disorders that frequently affect older people. Amongst the most common are the following:

- **Stroke**

   A stroke is caused by an interruption of the blood supply to the brain, usually through a blockage in the blood vessels, and this results in the death of certain brain cells. The effects on the person depend on which part of the brain these are in, but can include instability, incontinence, paralysis, partial blindness, speech difficulties and confusion of thought. Physiotherapy, speech and occupational therapy can all help and many people gradually recover almost completely, but a great deal of specialist support is needed, and organizations such as the Chest, Heart and Stroke Association and VOCAL (dealing with speech and communication problems) can give both practical advice and emotional help.

- **Parkinson's disease**

   This is a disorder of the part of the brain controlling muscular movement. It may be due to narrowing of the blood vessels, but often appears to have no known cause. It can result in a tremor in the hands or head and muscular stiffness affecting speech and movement. There are two main types of drug treatment that can control stiffness and shaking and there is detailed literature available from the Parkinson's Disease Society.

- **Emphysema and bronchitis**

   Both these are common lung diseases in older people that can occur separately or together. Both result in breathlessness because the damaged lungs fail to absorb enough oxygen and put a strain on the heart. A reduction in weight, plenty of rest, giving up smoking, plus swift diagnosis of any colds, coughs, flu or throat infections will all help. Drug treatments are not always so successful, although some improvement is possible, but antibiotics will keep infections under control. Again the CHSA has more detailed advice avaiable.

- **Heart disease**

   Heart failure is very common among older people. Many suffer from a narrowing of the arteries that supply the heart with blood or there may be damage to the valves or the muscles. The heart then fails to pump sufficient oxygen round the body, leading to breathlessness, general weakness and, in some cases, confused behaviour. Drug treatments can help and it is most important to see the doctor or specialist rather than just accepting such symptoms as part of getting older. Again, contact CHSA for advice and counselling.

● Arthritis

There are two common types of arthritis – rheumatoid, which affects the small joints of hands, feet, ankles, knees and elbows with swelling and pain in the connecting tissues, and osteoarthritis, a wearing through of the cartilage that covers bones where they meet at the joints, particularly knees, hips and spine. Treatments are available – including physiotherapy – to keep joints and limbs as supple as possible, so don't dismiss the signs as inevitable aches and pains of old age. The British Rheumatic and Arthritic Association and the Arthritis and Rheumatism Council can give specialized help.

● Cancer

Conditions such as cancer may require very intensive care at certain stages, but even so many patients are nursed at home. It is most important to have good professional support, particularly if drugs are needed to control pain. A hospice, especially if the older person is terminally ill, can give just the right backup, both practical and emotional. There are many helpful organizations now giving information on various aspects of cancer and its treatment including Cancerlink and BACUP (British Association of Cancer United Patients.)

● Alzheimer's disease

This is just one cause of the mental confusion that can affect older people in varying degrees. In Alzheimer's disease there is a deterioration of the brain tissue, which leads to changes in mood, memory and general behaviour, but there are many other reasons for dementia and mental frailty and in the next chapter these are examined in greater depth, along with hearing and sight impairment and speech difficulties. The Alzheimer's Disease Society is a recognized authority on the subject and has publications and local support groups.

There are obviously a great many other illnesses that can afflict older people, including motor neurone disease, diabetes and multiple sclerosis. Skin conditions such as eczema and psoriasis can also appear or worsen in older age.

Several books are available that give detailed medical information about symptoms, treatments and practical instructions on care. Particularly worth reading are *Take Care of Your Elderly Relative* by Dr Muir Gray and Heather McKenzie Lovat (Allen and Unwin, 1980) and *Caring for an Elderly Relative* by Dr M. Keith Thompson, a GP who has worked with elderly people and those who care for them (Positive Health Guide, Martin Dunitz/Macdonald Optima, 1986). Both books contain the type of medical information and instruction that unfortunately is often not passed on to patients or carers by the family GP or even hospital specialists. Armed with real knowledge about their elderly dependants' illness or disability, carers are in a much better position to both give and demand the right treatment.

Self-help health

As you will have noticed from this and previous chapters, a great deal of information and support is also available through the various voluntary organizations and self-help groups mentioned so far. These groups usually have the support of more enlightened doctors and specialists and produce extremely well-informed and medically accurate booklets, leaflets,
newsletters and magazines packed with advice and practical tips, plus the experience of both professionals and laymen. The Arthritis and Rheumatism Council, for instance, has a general information booklet called *Introducing Arthritis*, plus a series of more detailed leaflets on aspects such as back-ache, rheumatoid arthritis and new hip joints. Another booklet gives tips on keeping mobile and active in the home and

includes a variety of helpful gadgets and aids. Another example is the Parkinson's Disease Society which issues a booklet explaining causes, treatments and general care for patients and their families, written by a consultant neurologist, plus other helpful literature. The Chest, Heart and Stroke Association has a huge range of publications dealing with many disorders affecting older people. These include *Facts About High Blood Pressure, Overcoming Your Coronary, Stroke – Twenty questions and answers* and *Coronary After-Care*.

The CHSA also employs trained counsellors who can answer particular questions. The Volunteer Stroke Scheme arranges home visits from speech therapists for people who have suffered strokes and runs clubs that both older person and carer can attend. In fact, most of these organizations have local branch meetings to which carers can go, and where they can learn more about the particular condition affecting an elderly relative or friend. It is also a way of meeting others in the same situation, and gaining strength from the mutual support such friendships can give.

Many of these organizations are raising money to fund research into new treatments, cause and cure, so taking part is not only comforting on a personal level but because you know others will benefit too. Being involved with a local branch can be a very positive outlet for the knowledge and frustrations that carers share.

Training in nursing

When older people become ill, disabled and dependent there should be professional nursing help available to help with bathing, changing of dressings and colostomy bags, getting them in and out of bed and so on. As we've seen, such nursing help varies according to where you live, but even when services are good carers will usually find themselves dealing with a large part of the day-to-day nursing. However able they are, it stands to reason that they will need to have a knowledge of nursing techniques. They may be dealing with bed sores and leg ulcers. They may have to administer injections and they will almost certainly be handling a number of medicines, giving the correct dosage at the right times. Many must also know themselves how to change dressings and colostomy bags. Carers may also need to know about special diets and they will constantly be required to lift, turn and support an elderly relative during the course of each day and probably night, too. The wear and tear that this can have on the carer's own health is dealt with in Chapter 6, but some training in practical nursing could ease the situation for many.

In some areas nursing courses are already being provided for carers by the health authority. In Birmingham, for instance, the community nursing service arranges regular Home Care courses. These cover lifting and moving patients, incontinence problems, equipment and aids and practical demonstrations of nursing techniques. Various professionals are also invited along to talk, including physiotherapists, occupational therapists, health visitors specializing in geriatric care, district nurses, dieticians, speakers from social services and from the DHSS. This is an excellent example for other health authorities to follow, and the hope is that all will eventually provide similar training as community care – and at the same time home nursing – grows.

In the meantime very useful sources of nursing courses are the Red Cross and the St John's Ambulance Brigade. The Red Cross runs four types of courses, all helpful to carers at home. There is a Basic Nursing Course, which covers simple nursing techniques for use within the home, including moving and lifting of an invalid and catering for the general needs of frail, elderly people. There is also a Standard Nursing Course with more comprehensive coverage of skills such as giving a bed bath, dressing simple wounds, providing special diets and administering medicines. In the Advanced Nursing Course more serious illnesses and disabilities are covered, including looking after a paralysed or unconscious patient. Another course, Nursing for the Family, gives general advice and includes caring for a stroke victim.

These courses are available in all parts of the country and for a leaflet giving more details you should contact the British Red Cross central office (for their address, see page 147) or your local branch. The Red Cross also produces two helpful

handbooks with step-by-step picture guides to toiletting, lifting, feeding and many other aspects of home nursing, called
Caring for the Sick and *Practical Nursing*. It also has other
publications on aids for handicapped people and people in
wheelchairs. The local Red Cross branches, as well as social
services departments, can also loan out nursing aids from
smaller items such as drinking cups and air rings, to walking
frames, commodes and wheelchairs.

Rehabilitation after hospital

When an older person is discharged from hospital and sent
home another source of support and advice should be the
hospital staff. The occupational therapist, for instance, can
advise on what extra aids may be needed if mobility is decreasing and the hospital social worker on the local community
nursing services and care attendant schemes. Unfortunately,
as in every other area of caring, not everyone gets this sort of
help. Some old people are discharged at weekends or in the
evening with little or no warning to relatives or friends. Even
when a hospital has been very supportive to an inpatient,
with friendly staff and good standards of treatment, it may
still not do enough to successfully rehabilitate the patient and
advise the carer, yet, if this is done, it can have lasting good
effects. In *Caring* by Judith Oliver and Anna Briggs (Routledge
& Kegan Paul, 1985), a book relating the experiences of many
of those looking after disabled relatives, one says:

> 'It amazed me to find how a single aid (for example a small
> convenient bath hoist) could transform a bad situation into
> something manageable. Likewise, a few minutes instruction
> from the physiotherapist on how to get a disabled person to
> stand up from a sitting position made a world of difference to
> me. It saved my back, it helped my husband's self-esteem and
> it took the doubt and tension out of the manoeuvre.'

A carer wrote to me about the great difference that quite small
gadgets and aids can make to the quality of a dependant person's life and to the carer's. A knitting needle holder, for
instance, means an interest can be continued. Bath boards,
bath seats, non-slip mats, long-handled combs and sponges

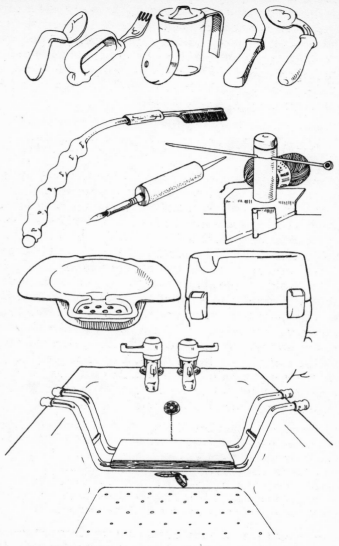

may mean they can manage washing, grooming and bathing with the minimum of help. There is also a wide range of special cutlery and kitchen equipment available through the hospital or social services department that can lead disabled people back, not only to feeding themselves, but also to carrying out simple cookery and kitchen tasks.

In some hospitals, such as the special unit in Sussex mentioned on page 94, time is spent building patients' potential *before* they return home so that they are immediately able to do more for themselves. This also stops the carer from falling into the trap of doing too much. Judith Oliver explains:

> 'Many dependants could do far more for themselves if properly trained. Hospitals often don't show older people how to get from bed to commode or make a cup of tea after they have recovered from a disabling illness. But often you don't know what efforts they can make until they try, and the carer has to be guided by the doctors as to what dependant people can undertake. Often people can improve, but carers may continue giving the same level of support as when they were discharged from hospital, maybe for 10 years. Without professional guidance carers can stay protective for far too long.'

Changing attitudes

Irene is one carer who decided to take the law into her own hands. After her father spent two years in the geriatric ward of one large teaching hospital she put forward various suggestions to the staff on how she thought the treatment of patients and relatives could be improved:

> 'I felt that young nurses training in geriatric wards were not taught how to answer questions that relatives may ask. In fact they sometimes treat them as though they are idiots, but relatives and those others who have been close to patients prior to their being admitted to hospitals can offer invaluable advice, guidance and clues to medical staff to assist in diagnosing patient's problems. Unfortunately a few hospital staff give the impression that any advice offered is an intrusion into their professional capabilities. But the exchange should be two-way. When you are desperately trying to cope with a mental or geriatric problem it would be nice if there was a 24-hour service available somewhere in the hospital. Someone to talk to helps a lot.
>
> 'There also seems to be a lack of communication at times between hospitals, social services and doctors. Also, if social workers have been helping someone with a problem, it would

be nice if they didn't always wait for carers to contact them but gave them a call sometimes to see if everything is all right at home.'

Irene and some other carers were asked along to the hospital to speak at a special seminar addressing hospital specialists, health visitors and nurses on the sort of support and information they would like to see available, especially for those about to be discharged.

Her efforts paid off, because now, among other improvements, the hospital has produced a booklet called *Going Home* which is given to patients and their friends and families as they are discharged.

Coping with incontinence

An area of great difficulty for both cared for and carers is incontinence. The former feel embarrassed, ashamed and frightened at this bodily loss of control; the latter must deal with the results, on top of all the other jobs they do, often many times a day. Sleep and daytime rest is disturbed, clothing, bedding and furniture spoilt and laundry and washing multiplies. It can also involve carers in a degree of intimacy with the dependant that can be deeply distressing for both of them. Yet, as with so many aspects of looking after an elderly person, carers are caught in a confusing situation. On the one hand you will sometimes want to scream with frustration, even anger, at the mess and constant work that incontinence can cause while, on the other hand, you will understand that it is not really the dependant person's fault and what he or she needs is loving support and sympathy, but this can often be hard to summon up.

Fred has been caring for his wife for 12 years since an operation for a tumour left her brain damaged and, as he puts it 'practically a cabbage.' Every now and then she slips into a coma and has to spend time in hospital.

'She is doubly incontinent. I have to wash on average 12–16 sheets, 3 blankets and 6–7 nightdresses every 24 hours. My day with her never begins or ends, it is continuous.

'I love her very much. That is why I look after her. It has

been suggested many times that I should put her in a home, but that to me is unthinkable. I am not in any way upset or depressed, but feel that we both have been here too long.'

Yet for Fred and carers like him there may be far more help and hope than they think. Incontinence is by no means inevitable in older age, and is far more responsive to treatment and therapy than is realized. There are many people working in this field now, and some hospitals even have special continence advisers working with both young and old afflicted in this way. That is why, just as with aches, pains and mental confusion, it is so important to have a proper diagnosis because incontinence can be the result of a treatable condition.

Infections of the urinary tract, constipation, drugs that reduce general mental awareness, bladder stones, too little fluid, prostate abnormalities, prolapse or stretching caused by childbirth can all cause incontinence. When muscles are weak, any involuntary action like a sneeze, coughing, crying or laughing can lead to what is called 'stress incontinence'. Also, when the older person has difficulty moving around it may not be possible for him or her to get to a toilet quickly enough.

Incontinence that is the result of mental confusion and senile dementia is especially difficult to deal with because it may not be possible to reason with older people or persuade them to take necessary action. But even here experts feel that much can be done to improve the situation and certainly to avoid the problems affecting carers like Fred. For example:

- Try and establish a routine of going to the toilet regularly during the day and last thing at night as nurses do in hospital.
- Ask your GP, social services department or hospital occupational therapist about various toilet aids, such as a raised seat (a device you fit to the toilet seat that raises the height of the seat helping the elderly person get on and off the toilet easily), a frame around the toilet or rails on the wall. Rails along hall walls can also help an older person make the journey to and from the toilet more quickly.
- Ask for help from a physiotherapist. Exercises can

strengthen the muscles to overcome incontinence, increase muscle control after a stroke and improve general mobility.

- Ask for the advice of a hospital gynaecologist, as a simple operation may bring back control for women whose muscles have been stretched in childbirth.
- If the toilet is upstairs, or some distance from the room where the older person spends most time, ask the social services department or local Red Cross to supply a commode.
- Clothing can be adapted to make it easier for an older person to act quickly, with velcro replacing buttons and zips, for instance. The district or community nurse can advise on this.
- Include vegetables, fruit, cereals and foods with plenty of fibre in the diet to ease constipation as this can cause pressure on the bladder and a type of diarrhoea.

- Don't restrict fluids, as this will lead to dehydration and can even *cause* incontinence, but give more liquids in the morning and afternoon than later in the day to avoid night disturbance.
- At night, provide a commode or potty, make sure that there is a lamp beside the bed and, if necessary, you could mark the route to the toilet with luminous tape.
- For someone who is bedridden or has great difficulty getting out of bed, a bed pan, plastic urine bottle or urine dish should be within easy reach.

If some accidents are inevitable, take precautions. Protect furniture by using washable covers over dustbin liners, for instance. There are some excellent protective sheets available, such as the Kylie sheet, that can absorb urine without the surface of the sheet becoming wet. There are various preparations to help deodorize commodes, clothing and so on. Incontinence pants and pads are sometimes available free through the community nursing service of the health authority, and in some areas there is a free laundry service for sheets and other bedding. Do seek out all the help and information you can get rather than simply accepting this problem. Particularly good is the Disabled Living Foundation Incontinence Information Service. DLF has a special adviser on this subject and she has written a book called *Incontinence* that explores the whole subject in great depth.

Checking on medicines

As such a bewildering variety of drugs are prescribed nowadays for both physical and mental ailments, carers need to keep a careful check on which are to be taken when and for what. They also need to watch for any adverse as well as beneficial side-effects. Some drugs can cause other symptoms to develop such as rashes, swelling or mental confusion and it is important to know about these so that correct actions can be taken. In particular, many of the tranquillizers prescribed for depression, anxiety or excitability can lead to other mood and behaviour disturbances, so that what is supposed to be a

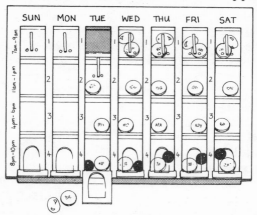

cure can eventually turn into another cause.

A good GP should advise on what to expect, discuss worries about effects and try a different drug if a particular type does not suit the older person. The various voluntary organizations dealing with disabilities can also advise and MIND has a leaflet pointing out the possible adverse effects of tranquillizers.

It is also a good idea to keep pills in a safe place, clearly labelled with a daily timetable showing how many need to be taken and at what time each day. This will be especially useful for older people who live alone and have to deal with medication themselves. Otherwise they may become confused, and take too many or too few. Here are some other useful suggestions:

● Keep a record card, writing down details of which drugs

are to be taken, the dosage, when they should be adminis-
tered and what they are for, ticking them off throughout
the day.

- Buy some of the clear plastic containers used in hospitals,
  putting each dosage inside and clearly labelling the con-
  tainer with the time of day they are to be taken (this is
  especially suitable for older people living alone.)
- Buy tablet boxes from the chemist or get some through the
  community health service. These are divided into com-
  partments for days of the week and times of the day and
  make it easier to keep check on what needs to be taken
  when.

Those over pensionable age will get prescriptions free under
the NHS. Hospital prescriptions are also issued free of
charge.

Caring for the very sick

There is naturally a difference between the daily routine of
caring for someone who is disabled, and therefore has problems getting around, and the older person who has become
acutely ill and is perhaps dying. Many will go into a hospital,
hospice or nursing home at this stage, but some families and
older people choose home care because they would rather
they spent their last days together in the security and comfort
of familiar surroundings. Naturally this is a very demanding
task for carers and one that needs a great deal of backup from
hospital, GP, the community nursing service and any
neighbourhood care attendant schemes.

It's also extremely important for carers to know what to
expect during the course of the illness and how to cope with
the changing situation. Two very useful booklets are produced by Cancerlink called *Taking Time* and *Caring for the Very
Sick Person at Home*. These include some practical tips for making the ill person comfortable. For instance:

- A sheepskin rug, duvet or eiderdown may be more comfortable to lie on if the patient is rather bony and finds the
  bed hard.

- A handbell beside the bed is helpful if a person is weak and hasn't got the strength or energy to call.
- The mouth tends to become dry and uncomfortable, so sweets, a glass of water with a drinking straw, a thermos with warm or cold drink or wet wipes should be kept by the bed. Crushed ice, flavoured or plain, can also be refreshing.
- If solid foods are difficult to eat or digest, fluids can be enriched by adding ice-cream to a milk shake or a beaten egg to soup.
- It's important that when a person has constant or regular bouts of pain these are kept under control with medication, rather than waiting for the pain to start.
- Sights and sounds continue to be important, however ill someone is. Something to look at such as a view from the window, a mobile or favourite picture and a radio or tape to listen to, can be comforting and reassuring.

Cancerlink also stresses how important it is for carers to look after themselves. As the organization points out, professional workers are there to give support and it advises carers not to be afraid to ask questions if anything is bothering them, however trivial this may appear. Cancerlink points out:

'You the carers are going through a very stressful time yourselves. It is natural to feel anxious, fearful, sad and even bitter that this is happening to you and your family. You may feel helpless, you may be feeling tired and strained.

'These are normal feelings and ones you must not feel guilty about. The professionals are there to care about and support *you*. Talk to them about how you are coping. By looking after your own needs in this way you will be all the more able to look after your loved one.'

CHAPTER 5
A loss of sense

'To see a big strong man struck down like this is heart-rending. He was such a hardworking man and so independent and now has to depend on me so much.'

'To live with someone who doesn't know who you are or where she is is very stressful. She became more and more nasty tempered because she loathed a younger person doing what she used to do.'

Mental frailty

A great number of carers are coping with the added strain of mental confusion, senile dementia or some other loss of communication with the older person.

'An assault on the senses' is how senile dementia has been described and the words certainly sum up the effects on many carers. Some feel they are becoming mad themselves as they try to cope rationally and calmly with the increasingly illogical, bizarre and sometimes deeply upsetting responses of a disturbed older person. Many carers struggle on under great stress, denying to others and even to themselves the mental anguish and depression they are suffering but, as Kathy, the Family Welfare Association counsellor, points out, to face these emotions, and realize that they are both very common and very understandable, can be the first step towards finding some solutions and feeling better about the situation:

'Alzheimer's disease is a particularly tragic situation which makes communication very difficult, but too much denial goes on. It helps to acknowledge that the sufferers are ill and not just weird. It's also important to bear in mind that their behaviour is mostly beyond their control and that they are not doing it deliberately to be difficult.'

Once again, joining a support group where carers can talk to others coping with the same sorts of difficulties can bring about this kind of understanding and acceptance.

A personal experience

One such group was set up in London by a social worker specializing in supporting elderly people and their carers. Almost everyone there is coping with mental frailty of one sort or another in their dependants. In the case of Edith, for instance, her husband was knocked down by a car when he was 70. A clot formed on the brain and, after a period in a coma, he developed epilepsy and dementia.

'My whole day revolves around him. I stay in almost all the time because I couldn't just go out and leave him. I help him dress every day otherwise he will take two hours. I get him downstairs and then he sits and watches television while I get the lunch.

'At the moment he's more rational and goes to the Day Centre for a few hours twice a week, but some days he just doesn't want to go. He's lazy and I make him do things he doesn't want to do, like sticking the stamps on the Christmas card envelopes. I'm always thinking of ways and means. But this has been going on for nine years now. He's irritated when anyone comes visiting and that makes it uncomfortable. When he was younger he was so different. I do miss the company of others and how he used to be.'

One of the hardest things to bear in severe senile dementia is the fact that, in many cases, elderly people do not even know the people looking after them any more. Reg, married to his wife for 30 years, describes how she insists that he isn't her husband but her brother-in-law.

She began to lose all sense of time, and at night would put her coat on to go out. She would turn on the gas burners without lighting them, hide money all over the house and in pots and pans, socks and shoes. She tore cushion covers and paintings, and would walk out of the house and disappear for days.

In the book *Caring* by Judith Oliver and Anna Briggs (Routledge & Kegan Paul, 1985) a carer describes the effects her mother's growing mental confusion has on her:

> 'At first I didn't understand and thought she was just being difficult – which made me angry. Then again, the most soul-destroying aspect is the sheer inescapable boredom of it – not being able to communicate properly with her or get her to do what you want logically.
>
> 'Few people can understand the sense of desperation, left alone for long periods with a confused elderly person, unless they have done it themselves. It makes you say and do cruel things even though you love the person.'

Finding some solutions

Like Edith and John (whose experience looking after his wife with Alzheimer's disease is told on page 142) many carers do find ways of making the best of a very difficult situation and perhaps easing the problems of the older person.

The first step is to get a correct medical diagnosis. According to the Alzheimer's Disease Society, about half of all cases of senile dementia are caused by this condition, a brain disorder in which, for reasons as yet largely unknown, a number of brain cells cease to function.

The next most common cause of dementia is multi-infarct dementia, when a series of small strokes block the blood supply to an area of the brain, killing the cells. But there can be other conditions that, at first sight, have very similar symptoms even though the causes are very different and often treatable.

A GP should arrange for investigations and tests with various specialists if senile dementia is suspected. These should include:

- A neurologist – a specialist in disorders of the brain and nerve pathways.
- A geriatrician – a specialist in the illnesses suffered by elderly people.

- A psychiatrist – a specialist in mental illness.
- A psycho-geriatrician – a specialist in mental illness in elderly people, including senile dementia.

Among the disorders they will look for are infections, vitamin deficiencies, thyroid gland problems, heart disorders and brain tumours – all of which can affect the correct functioning of the brain in older people. Another important aspect to consider is depression, or some other form of mental illness. When younger people suffer from nervous breakdowns and anxiety states because of the stresses of life, successful treatments are often found. Yet, even though older people have more reason to experience stress, following bereavement and so on, their unhappiness and distress is frequently dismissed as senile dementia. Many might well respond to counselling, psychotherapy or short-term treatment with tranquillizers or anti-depressants in the same way that someone younger would.

In some cases mental disturbance is a direct side-effect of drugs being taken for a physical illness. These can affect the functioning of body and mind in quite drastic ways and (as stressed on page 76) side-effects should always be watched for very carefully. One carer told me how, after being prescribed a particular type of painkiller following a hospital operation, her mother was hallucinating and seeing insects walking up and down the wallpaper of her room. After a word with the nurses the drug was changed and the hallucinations stopped.

Two further cases illustrate even more clearly how essential thorough examinations and careful diagnoses are when considering senile dementia. A man in his seventies who had a fall was left physically feeble and scarcely knowing where or who he was. His GP diagnosed him as suffering from senile dementia and sent him to hospital for long-term care. However, tests revealed that he had a severe heart problem. After an operation his confusion disappeared and he was able to return home and look after himself.

A woman caring for her elderly mother found that her mother's health began to deteriorate after the death of her only son in a car accident. She was diagnosed by the doctor as suffering from senile dementia and he said that there was nothing he could do. The carer says:

> 'All the symptoms of senile dementia were there, no sense of time or place, memory lapses, sleeping in the daytime and awake at night. Often I was up all night and then had to go to work next day.
>
> 'After one particularly bad weekend I called the doctor as I was getting really desperate. A locum came and he sent mother to hospital. They decided she was not suffering from senility but her heart was beating too slowly and suggested that a pace-maker would help.
>
> 'It was the most astonishing thing. A day or two later I could see a difference and within a fortnight she was a different person. Her memory was back, she knew where she was, who she was and so on. It was a real miracle. We had four lovely years until she had a bout of 'flu and just slipped away one morning.'

Not everyone will be so fortunate, but at least by insisting on a thorough diagnosis you can be quite sure that there are not other treatable, physical and mental causes for the older person's disturbed emotions and behaviour.

Helpful tips

Even when senile dementia or mental fraility of some type is medically confirmed, there are still many ways in which life can be made more bearable for both carer and cared for.

Just as training in practical nursing skills is needed when the older person has a physical illness, techniques can be learned that minimize some of the difficulties that can arise. Here are some suggestions from carers:

- It is often possible to talk more than is realized. There are different levels of insight, with sudden small breakthroughs in understanding. If they ask what is the matter, say they are ill and that something has gone wrong with their memory. Always speak clearly, slowly and simply.
- Use body language such as touch, gesture and warm looks as many confused and mentally frail people respond better to these than to anything else.

- Try not to go along with muddled thinking, but correct it as tactfully as possible, repeating a point where necessary and using an object or picture to confirm information. For instance, wearing your coat shows you are going out.
- Use memory aids wherever possible, such as clocks set at the correct time, calendars which clearly state date, day and year, room names on doors with an illustration, photographs of family and friends dotted around. These all help the older person keep track of identity, place and time.
- Pay extra attention to safety, keeping furniture in predictable places, watching for slippery mats, floors and any other hazards. Make sure all medicines, cleaning fluids and bleach are out of the way, saucepan handles turned inwards on the hob and safety devices attached to gas cookers.

Particular problems

When carers of confused, elderly people talk together they find that there seem to be shared patterns to their charges' behaviour. Dressing back to front and in unsuitable clothing, wandering round the house or further from home, and becoming disturbed at night all seem to be very common. One carer's wife regularly woke in the night and wanted to go to the shops. Another would get up and climb into bed with other members of the household. A carer already worn out by the day's demands will find it very difficult to remain rational and calm. Without in any way underestimating the difficulties, there are practical solutions that ease some of the emotional stresses. For example:

● **Dressing**
It helps to lay one clean set of clothes out in the order they have to go on, putting others out of sight. Buttons can be replaced with Velcro fastening and shoes can be the slip-on type. Praising appearance, making sure hair is regularly styled and set and that older people are clean and tidy helps their self-esteem and can lead to improved behaviour.

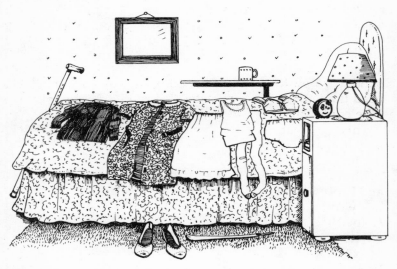

● **Wandering**
This can be due to excess of energy, so activities during the day such as visits to a day centre or simple jobs in the house can help. If they are searching for things, keep personal possessions on view and have a predictable routine. Locks may be needed at the bottom of doors, where they are less noticeable, and an identity bracelet or card will ensure a quick return if the older person wanders a long way away.

● **Night disturbance**

The older person may be looking for the toilet, so make sure he or she goes before bedtime. A bed-side lamp may comfort the older person who wakes up frightened and confused and, rather like a baby, a gentle talk and cuddle will reassure, but this can be a lot to ask of carers who are themselves exhausted and in need of sleep. More activity during the day may help, and failing all else sleeping tablets from the GP for both carer *and* cared for. Sleep is essential for mental and physical well-being and cannot be sacrificed because in the end everyone will suffer.

All carers I have talked to have stressed the need to keep a sense of humour if at all possible. Even though the situation is often so sad, many things the older people do *are* funny and laughing with them can defuse and lighten the situation. When one husband's wife got in a muddle and tried to put her knickers on over her head he'd smile and say, 'What are you trying to do that for?' and they'd both laugh. Another husband tells how his wife liked making cups of tea, but one day used the floor cloth by mistake. 'It just fell in', she told him. 'She could still joke', he remarks, affectionately.

There are many specialist publications now giving detailed help in coping with senile dementia that make essential reading for carers coping with this illness. The Health Education Authority, for instance, have a booklet entitled *Who Cares?* and Professor Elaine Murphy, a leading specialist in the field, has written a paperback entitled *Dementia and Mental Illness* (Papermac, 1986.)

The Alzheimer's Disease Society can also give a great deal of expert help. There are local branches of the society in many parts of the country and a wide range of literature is available. This includes a booklet packed with information called *Caring for the Person with Dementia* (for the Alzheimer's Disease Society's address see page 150.)

Hard of hearing

Another reason for confusion in the elderly may well be that

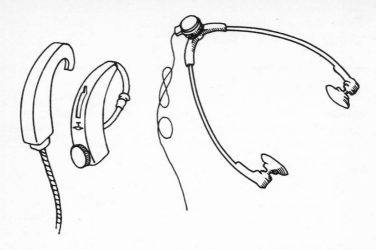

one or more of their senses are becoming less efficient but that this is going undetected.

It is very common for hearing to deteriorate and for no one to realize. If older people make odd replies to questions, mis-understand what is said, don't seem interested in things going on around them or ignore telephones, door bells and other domestic happenings, then impaired hearing may be the cause and we just put it down to something else. The deaf-ness may not be long-term. For instance, there may be a build-up of wax in the ear that can be syringed out by a nurse or GP at the local surgery. If there are more serious reasons for the deafness then it may be necessary for an examination to be carried out by an ear, nose and throat specialist in hospital.

A hearing aid may be recommended or a simple operation might improve matters. There are now several types of hear-ing aid available through the NHS, with receivers worn on the chest or with plastic attachments behind the ear. The ear, nose and throat department can advise on these.

If older people are mobile and mentally alert but getting quite deaf, it might also be a good idea for them to attend lip-reading classes. You can find out if these exist in your area through the social services department or a local centre for the deaf.

There are a variety of other ways that carers have found communication can be improved when a person has poor hearing:

- Make sure your face – especially your mouth – can be clearly seen in a good light while speaking.
- If hearing is better on one side than the other, always speak from this side.
- Speak clearly and slowly, using short sentences, but don't shout. This distorts both voice and mouth and impede's understanding.
- Use gestures and objects to reinforce what you are saying, pointing to the teapot when suggesting tea or the clock when discussing time. Sign language can also be useful, especially when deafness is profound.

There are many practical aids available and these are often free to those on a low income. You can find out more about these from the local social services department or ear, nose and throat hospital department and there are some social workers now specializing in working with deaf people

Door bells and alarm clocks can be fitted with flashing lights so that the deaf person can have an audio one replaced with a visual one. There is a television adaptor available that provides a separate volume control to an ear-piece, allowing someone whose hearing is impaired to adjust the sound without affecting others in the room. There is also a very ingenious device called the loop induction system that creates a magnetic field within which those wearing a hearing aid can receive sound signals from TV, radio or record player without the background noises in the room. The telephone inductive coupler is designed to improve telephone sound quality for the hard of hearing. The aid is built into the telephone and works in conjunction with ear-level hearing aids. Demonstrations are available at British Telecom offices.

The Royal National Institute for the Deaf and other voluntary organizations for those with imparied hearing have a great deal of useful literature, including advice on aids that can make life easier for both carers and older people. There are also local branches and clubs to join.

Loss of sight

Like hardness of hearing, not being able to see clearly can creep up on an older person without anyone realizing. This may be because the eyes are becoming less efficient with age or because of a treatable disorder. Some diseases affecting the eyes may show few symptoms at first but have very damaging effects in the long term. Older people therefore should take advantage of the free check-up by an optician that they are entitled to every year. Any unusual symptoms such as blurred vision or flashing lights should be checked immediately with your doctor.

Cataracts are very common as people get older and can be removed in a simple operation. Glaucoma is another common disorder affecting sight, and, caught in its early stages, is treatable with tablets and eyedrops.

Pensioners are entitled to vouchers for spectacles under the NHS and, for many, their sight can be improved considerably, but for some the deterioration is such that they may

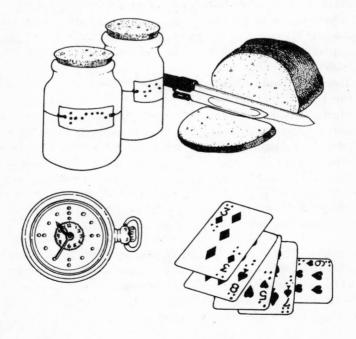

need to be registered as partially sighted or blind. There are certain advantages in doing this because various aids and new sources of help then become available. A social worker may be allocated who can give specialist advice and a rehabilitation or mobility officer who can give practical help in managing day-to-day living. There are many extras that can make life much more pleasant for the older people and those caring for them:

- Clocks, watches, devices for measuring the liquid being poured into a cup and a number of other household gadgets are available. Many are marked with braille or Moon (a raised alphabet) for numbers and letters.
- Talking books are a wonderful source of entertainment and interest. Tapes with full-length books recorded on them are available post free from the British Talking Book Service and the National Listening Library along with free use of cassette machines. These may also be supplied by your local library. There is a Talking Newspaper Association, too, that records tapes of newspaper contents.
- A telephone is invaluable for someone with failing sight. Social services may be able to pay for this, but you can also apply for help from the British Telephones for the Blind Fund.
- You may also be able to get a radio through the Wireless for the Bedridden Society.
- Modern technological aids may be a bit beyond many older people, but a tape recorder can help in correspondence, making notes or even keeping a daily diary.
- Simple sign language may be learned by carer and cared for to help with communication. Don't forget how important body language becomes too, with touching, hugs and physical guidance giving both practical and emotional support.

Failing sight at any age is a frightening experience and when people are old there may be less ability to adjust and a great deal of anxiety over the effects. The Royal National Institute for the Blind have many helpful leaflets and booklets including one specifically aimed at older people.

Communication disorders

An offshoot of many of the illnesses affecting older people is difficulty with speech and understanding. Speech can be affected through muscular and nerve disorders such as Parkinson's disease and multiple sclerosis, but the most common cause is a stroke.

After a stroke speech can be affected in two ways. In some patients it is slurred and indistinct or even completely absent, but the patient can read, write and understand what is said perfectly. This is called dysarthria and responds to treatment. The second possibility, dysphasia or aphasia, is much more common and is due to damage to the part of the brain that controls all language processes. This can affect the older person's ability to speak, understand speech, read or write. This condition occurs in nearly half the patients who suffer paralysis in the right side of the body after a stroke, but hardly ever among those who are paralysed on the left. Some cases are mild but in others speech is painfully slow and halting and recovery slow.

However old they are, people should be encouraged to keep working hard at recovery and every possible source of help brought in to support both the older person and the carer. The most important of these is the speech therapist who should be contacted through the GP, hospital specialist or community health service of the local authority. Speech therapy and various communication exercises may also be available through a local day centre or stroke club. There are also organizations that can help with speech problems relating to particular disorders. The Disabled Living Foundation has a guide to communication aids and the Chest Heart and Stroke Association has two useful publications called *Learning to Speak Again After a Stroke* and *A Time to Speak*. VOCAL is an umbrella organization that can put you in touch with a speech therapist, if this proves difficult, and also the relevant organization for different types of speech and communication difficulties. A particularly useful organization is Action for Dysphasic Adults (ADA) who produce a series of booklets on helping patients learn to read, write, understand and communicate again. There is a great deal that family and friends can do at home, and ADA gives the following advice:

- The patient may not be able to understand well, but he or she is not stupid. This is a breakdown of language and not mental deterioration.
- Don't allow anyone to patronize, talk down or treat older people as children, discussing them as if they aren't there. Understanding may be greater than is apparent and this treatment can increase resentment and frustration.
- Talk more slowly than usual and use clear, simple, short sentences without unnecessary words, including familiar names and phrases wherever possible.
- Encourage speech, but don't push too hard. Try to ask questions needing 'yes' or 'no' answers and use gestures and facial expressions to convey meaning.

The various aids available to help with communication can be seen at Communications Aids Centres run by the DHSS and the Royal Association for Disability and Rehabilitation (RADAR). Some are sophisticated electrical instruments and computers, others are more simple. For instance, communication charts use pictures and words to identify objects. These are available through speech therapists or you can make your own. You can also use sign language and the speech therapist will know if a local course is available. But most therapists prefer to concentrate on improving speech and understanding. With time a great deal of progress is possible, so do persevere and encourage because end results can be so rewarding.

Keeping in touch

Keeping older people in touch with those around them and the world outside is important for carer as well as dependant. Hanging on to the precious moments when there is communication will also strengthen you when coping with all the more difficult times.

Edith, whose experience looking after her mentally confused husband is told at the beginning of this chapter, finds that her husband is more lucid when he wakes early in the morning. So she uses this opportunity to talk to him.

> 'For those couple of hours I seem to get through to him, but then an hour or so later he will have forgotten what we talked about. During the day I try and find things to interest him as much as possible. I keep talking to him and make him read and think. Walking stimulates the circulation, and that helps the brain.
>
> 'He's always loved horses and betting and still likes watching it on TV, so I try and find books on the life stories of jockeys to read. I also make him do things he doesn't want to do. I give him a pen and paper, for instance, and suggest he writes some letters.'

At a hospital in Sussex the staff concentrate on rehabilitating older people after all illness, whether it is mental or physical. In the day centre there is speech therapy, hairdressing, art therapy, gym, cookery, remedial games and even gardening. Patients grow grapes in the hospital gardens, which are later made into the hospital wine.

Little touches make all the difference, like encouraging older people to try and walk rather than pushing them about in wheelchairs, or *asking* their names rather than looking at a label on their wrists. Staff take time to talk and listen to the older people, to encourage communication and alertness of mind.

Reminiscence projects

Like other such forward-looking hospitals, this particular hospital also practises reminiscence therapy, which has been found to have remarkable effects on mentally frail older people. Instead of being told that thinking and talking about the past is bad, they are actively encouraged to do so.

Many older people have a much better grasp of long-term than short-term memory and by going back to times in the past recover a feeling of their own identity and, at the same time, a better awareness of reality and the present time. They also feel that their lives have had value because others are showing an interest. In some reminiscence projects photo-

graphs and mementoes are collected, memories are taped and written down, exhibitions mounted and booklets produced. But even if there aren't ambitious results like these, just talking over the old days and seeing films and photographs of the local area as it used to be can stimulate and enliven older people in a remarkable way.

There are also projects devoted to older people of a different culture, for instance Caribbean or Chinese. These older people may have lost touch with their roots – even with their families – and reawakening memories of their past with its different traditions and language can help them regain a sense of themselves and their place in life.

Sources of comfort

An important source of comfort and means of communication for older people can be pets. Many studies are now finding that the physical comfort of stroking a dog or cat and remembering to care for them and feed them, leads to improvement in the physical health and mental stability of the owner. There is even an organization called PAT, which

arranges for owners of dogs with suitable temperaments to
make regular weekly visits to old people in hospital or at
home. Dogs are also being used, increasingly, as companion-
able helpers for disabled people as well as guide dogs for the
deaf and blind. The Society for Companion Animal Studies
(SCAS) has an interesting leaflet on the subject with a report
of one study which examined the effects of giving pet
budgerigars to older people.

> 'What the study showed was that the pleasure the birds gave
> to the owners amounted almost to a new lease of life. The
> older people quickly formed a very strong attachment to their
> pets. The study proved conclusively their value in a very
> noticeable way – the birds were far more rewarding com-
> panions than the one-way dialogue with the television.'

Another carer mentions the real importance of spiritual comfort for the older person. This will not apply to everyone, but
for some the support of the local church or some other
religious organization can make a great deal of difference.
This may be in purely practical ways, for instance, by church
members calling, sitting with and talking to the older people,
or it may be by giving them hope and comfort in more
spiritual terms. For both carer and cared for this can give a
sense of meaning to the experience that sees them through.

CHAPTER 6
The health of the carer

'I was very worried towards the end that mum would be bedridden and I would have to nurse her. With my back problems that would have been very difficult.'

'I was caring for my father, working and trying to keep some sort of order in two households. I became very tired, lost weight and felt permanently emotionally isolated.'

Effects on the body

One of the major dilemmas that carers face is that, in coping with another's disability, whether mental, physical or both, they may become ill or disabled themselves. Research on the subject shows that there are three main reasons for carers suffering physical ill effects:

- Many carers are already older themselves. At a time of life when they might well be needing some special care in their own right, they are, instead, making huge efforts to look after someone else.
- Caring involves physical stress that can be damaging. The most common complaints are back pain, exacerbation of arthritis and gynaecological problems, such as prolapse, often caused by moving, lifting and supporting a disabled and even immobile older person.
- Having reached a stage where a visit to doctor, outpatients' department, physiotherapist or hospital specialist is needed, carers' duties at home often prevent them from doing this or taking advantage of the treatment available.

One study on the effects of caring was carried out by the Association of Carers. The Association found that carers are often expected to carry out tasks alone that would be seen as beyond the capabilities of many professionals. The report comments:

> 'It is interesting to note that in a guidance book on back pain produced by the Royal College of Nursing the assumption throughout is that *two* people will be lifting, but this is seldom the case with home nursing.
>
> 'When treatment is offered many carers say they cannot find alternative care for their dependants when a hospital bed is available. Others say they are unable to comply with the surgeon's instructions that they do no lifting or pulling for a period of time after an operation.'

The Association of Carers comes across many examples of these situations. One carer fell while lifting her 16 stone husband into his wheelchair when the hoist broke. She had to continue in excrutiating pain as no alternative care for anyone under 65 years old was available in the area. Another woman has to call the police three times a day to help her husband onto the lavatory. He had polio 20 years ago and now has multiple sclerosis and there are no other sources of aid available in the remote rural area where they live.

One carer I talked to called Beatrice is in her seventies and is looking after her mother of 98. Though her mother was barely able to walk when she came to live with Beatrice and her husband five years ago, her physical condition has improved a good deal with Beatrice's care. She is, however, mentally confused and this means she needs constant supervision, as well as help with bathing, washing, dressing and going to the toilet. Now Beatrice herself is ill and has recently had an operation for cancer and developed an arthritic hip.

> 'The doctor says I shouldn't really be looking after my mother at all, but I promised my father I would when he was dying some years ago, and I know she couldn't manage alone. We have a break once a year when mother goes into hospital, but I must admit it is a strain.'

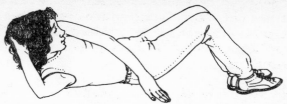

Lie on the floor with your knees up and feet together and place your hands behind your head. Lift your shoulders up off the floor and stretch your left arm across your body and place it on the floor beside your right hip. Repeat with your right arm and then keep alternating each arm.

Sit on the floor with your knees up, feet together and hands behind your head. Twist your body and bend at the hips so that your right elbow touches your left knee. Repeat, touching your right knee with your left elbow and then keep alternating each elbow.

Learning new strengths

These may be extreme cases, but, in reality, there are thousands of carers who have to call upon huge reserves of physical strength to simply turn someone in bed, heaving them up onto pillows or supporting them as they get out of bed or walk to the toilet or bathroom. I remember when my own father was seriously ill, he collapsed after climbing the stairs. I could not manage to lift him and he could not get to his feet. In the end we got him to the bedroom between us – me supporting him as he shuffled on his knees across the floor. It then took us half an hour to get him into bed. Nurses could have shown me the right way to do it, but in an emergency like this there is no way to find out. By doing things the wrong way I not only caused extra distress and discomfort for my father, but no doubt put damaging strains on my own body.

It is for these reasons that Christine Darby, a carer herself for many years, wrote her book *Keeping Fit While Caring* (Family Welfare Association, 1984 – for their address, see page 143.) With the help of a physiotherapist she has devised a series of exercises that strengthen neck, shoulder and back muscles.

'The incentive to write this book has come after spending many years regularly exercising to get my troublesome back strong enough to be able to lift my increasingly disabled husband. I have been told once too often how "lucky" I am to be able to do it.

'Other friends tell me how irritating it is to find that every time they strain or tear a muscle and sally forth bandaged and slung ready to receive unending cries of sympathy and concern, they are met with anxious enquiries as to: "How is mum, dad, Mabel, Ted, Janet or whoever, coping?" '

There is no doubt that carers have to be a tough and resilient lot, Christine concludes, but she suggests that by following a regular exercise programme it is possible to minimize injury and strain.

She also emphasizes the importance of a healthy diet, and shows in words and pictures the correct ways to help someone stand up, pick them up from the floor, turn them in bed, fit hoist seats and give a bath, both conventionally and under a blanket. There are also some useful tips that have been culled from practical experience. For instance, because of their efforts many carers develop stress incontinence. In her book Christine suggests exercises to strengthen rectal and pelvic muscles and recommends that no lifting should be done when the bladder is full.

Effects on the mind

It is not only the *physical* well-being of carers that can be badly affected by the tasks of caring, but their *mental* and *emotional* health, too. Various studies have found that, with or without the added strains of mental confusion or senile dementia in older people, carers are frequently deprived at every level of human need. The diagram shows the needs that should be

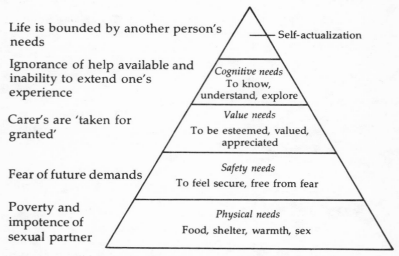

Life is bounded by another person's needs — Self-actualization

Ignorance of help available and inability to extend one's experience — *Cognitive needs* To know, understand, explore

Carer's are 'taken for granted' — *Value needs* To be esteemed, valued, appreciated

Fear of future demands — *Safety needs* To feel secure, free from fear

Poverty and impotence of sexual partner — *Physical needs* Food, shelter, warmth, sex

Maslow's hierachy of human need – you will see that carers are deprived in some way on each level.

fulfilled to maintain a reasonably satisfying life, and what the reality often is for carers.

The Association of Carers' report on the health of carers states that:

'Loss of a confidence has been shown to have a devastating effect on carers. Where the dependant is a spouse, keeping up the pretence of normality and absence of stress, with no one to whom one can unburden oneself, the strain can be enormous.

'This experience is also felt in other caring relationships, for example when a wife caring for an elderly parent is told by her husband that she must not expect help or when other siblings flatly refuse to take part in the care of an elderly relative. Those to whom one would expect to turn for empathy and understanding, leave one in the lurch.'

There are other major causes of depression in carers. For example:

- The total submersion of your own very real needs and preferences to those of another.
- The unhelpful attitude of some local authorities when seeking advice and support.
- Lack of money and, in many cases, real poverty.
- The unending repetition of practical tasks, many of them of an intimate and sometimes distressing nature.
- The constant company of someone who may be anxious, confused or seriously mentally ill.

The confusion of the resulting emotions pulls carers to and fro between guilt, anger, resentment, love, concern and conscientious care. These conflicting emotions can, in turn, deepen depression and may even, in some carers, lead to a mental breakdown.

Keeping sane

So, as well as keeping physically fit, it is essential for carers to encourage and preserve their own mental health. Although the difficulties you face are very real, there are ways to keep mind and emotions in better working order. One carer who wrote to me had two children, one a baby, when her 75-year-old mother-in-law came to live with her and her husband. She has since had to cope not only with her mother-in-law's mental and physical ill-health, but with a husband who has inherited the same depressive temperament.

'As well as being mentally ill, my mother-in-law also had physical frailties. She lived until she was 85 and for all that time I did not know that her peculiar highs and depressions were due to her illness. I thought I caused them.

'My husband, too, had always been very moody and irritable, often withdrawn, critical and demanding. Now, at 70, he is constantly low, afraid to go out, afraid to have people in and turning his obsessional qualities towards physical ill health. He is terribly dependent and stands and cries if I have 'flu.

'Finally, last year, I went and told a new, young female doctor in our practice how violent I felt about the circumstances. She, wonderful woman, listened to my outpourings once a week and then made me an appointment with a psychiatrist.

'This helped me get my thoughts into perspective. To retain my own sanity, she said, I must get out each day and, if possible, go away occasionally – perhaps to stay with my daughter. This has helped enormously. I also practise relaxation and meditation and I'm doing a postal course on Buddhism.'

Finding help

As is too often the case, this carer had to see the psychiatrist privately because of the long waiting lists for these services in the NHS. But finding someone to talk to, whether this is a therapist, counsellor, the leader of a support group, GP, social worker or friend, is often vital in sorting out some of the mental turmoil that can result from constant caring.

One counsellor who works regularly with carers, individually and in groups, points out that the experience can stunt their own mental growth.

'Some simply live *through* the older person, becoming so identified with him or her that they take on the same attitudes and forget all about themselves as individuals. It can be a bit like a mother and baby – they are so close that they feel they are part of each other. Carers can go back to an earlier parent/child relationship, forgetting who is who. They can be quite unaware that this is happening, but others can see it. By talking within a group, with a counsellor or with a friend they can look at the situation more objectively.

'The isolation of caring can make matters worse. By getting out and sharing experiences, other people may be able to point out what carers cannot recognize themselves.'

Kathy Weir of the Family Welfare Association support group gives couple counselling. This involves talking with both the carer and the dependant together, rather as in marriage guidance counselling or family therapy. Kathy explains:

'Strong emotions can be experienced on both sides of this particular partnership for different reasons. Carers may feel resentment, anger, grief and sadness at their situation; dependants may feel fear about losing their independence and faculties, plus envy of the person who is able bodied and able to get out.

'I spent nine months working with one couple, a woman and her aunt. The carer couldn't go out easily and when she did her aunt would cross-examine her. Because resentment had built up on both sides, conversation had stopped. Through counselling we were able to open it up again. Together they were able to reach an "I won't do this if you

won't do that" agreement. The niece developed more understanding of her aunt's insecurities and fears, and the aunt acknowledged how she blackmailed her and, in fact, could do far more than she let on. She learned she didn't need to do this any more. She realized her niece loved her and is going to go on looking after her. She didn't need to play silly games and act more dependant and defenceless than she really was.

'Equally, the carer learned that if she didn't like something her aunt did or said, she must tell her. She also had to accept that her aunt might have a heart attack whether she was there or not. Up till then she had held back from taking risks, feeling like so many other carers that if anything happened it would all be her fault.'

It is obviously more difficult, even impossible, to work together like this if the dependant has become severely mentally confused or if carers live in an isolated rural area where there are no counselling services available and it would be difficult to start a support group. For you, the following advice given by counsellors and carers in coping with some of the more commonly experienced emotions will be especially helpful.

Accepting the anger

As we've seen already, it is very common for carers to feel a great deal of anger about their situation and what often appear to be unfair demands made on them by their dependants and the rest of the family. One carer admits to throwing an incontinence pad across the room. Others feel that they have to restrain themselves from pushing or even hitting an older relative and are afraid that one day this will happen. 'My worst fear is that in temper I might hurt my dear wife,' wrote one carer to me. May Jones, a counsellor who has worked with several groups says:

'They'll say things like, "We all have our cross to bear," but underneath can be full of anger. A lot of feelings remain masked and pushed down because carers think they are not allowed to have any anger or "bad" emotions at all. If you think anger is bad, then you either bottle it up or suffer terrible regrets afterwards, but anger is a normal reaction in this situation. Everyone feels angry about all sorts of things, and carers often have every right to feel rage and stamp or throw a cushion.

'Ordinary families scream and shout at each other and so will carer and cared for now and then. They don't have to feel 100 per cent perfect, we all make mistakes. The older person may at times be very angry, so why shouldn't the carer? On the other hand, it isn't helpful to get into a pattern of anger, either.'

Humorous acceptance can be one way of dealing with anger. For instance, one carer found it very irritating the way her mother who had dementia muttered all the time, but snapping and getting angry did not stop what appeared to be an incurable sympton of the older person's illness. Eventually this carer was able to move onto acceptance. She just smiled, didn't fight against her mother's behaviour and gradually found her anger alleviated. The following are other suggestions from counsellors and carers:

- When really furious, get away for a few minutes on your own. Go into another room and punch a cushion; if there is the privacy, scream and shout; or simply sit and concentrate on breathing evenly and relaxing both body and mind.
- Be practical and down-to-earth about your feelings. You are working in a very difficult position and you must give yourself permission to feel like this occasionally.
- Forgive yourself. Getting angry doesn't mean you are a horrible person. Such feelings are totally understandable.
- If at all possible, explore your earlier relationship with the older person. There may be all sorts of buried and unexpressed feelings that are being triggered off again and which need bringing out and resolving.

Dealing with guilt

Feelings of guilt will often revolve around, 'If only I hadn't done or said so and so,' or, 'If only I had'. Anger and feelings of violence can make you feel unspeakably guilty, sometimes to the point where you feel you can't go on. But, in the view of many experienced counsellors, carers often tend to be over-conscientious, self-effacing people anyway, easily prone to guilt. They may always have been the responsible, caring person and got stuck in this role. In fact, carers can often feel *too* responsible. You may even encourage the complete dependence of another person, because you need to be needed, but, as carers and counsellors agree, there are times when, for everyone's good, you have to let go.

Guilt can also leave carers open to manipulation – another very common experience. Particularly when carers are dealing with people who are genuinely frail and disabled, it can be difficult to recognize this for what is is. A carer wanted to go on holiday without her husband because he was incontinent, but because he didn't wish to be cared for by someone else she cancelled the trip. In an extreme example, a newly married daughter went on sleeping with her mother at night to avoid causing her distress. As May Jones points out:

> 'If manipulation is left unchecked then it can get worse and worse. A precedent has to be set and after that it becomes easier. One member of our support group, like many others, had great difficulty in getting along because her mother made such a fuss.
>
> 'After a few weeks in the group this carer was able to tackle her mother. They talked about the problem and the daughter asked her mother how she would feel if she were in her position. They shouted a bit, but that released much of the tension between them.
>
> 'When she had stood up to her mother, the daughter felt very relieved. The risk had been taken and nothing very terrible had happened. The mother stopped grumbling, and even agreed to spend the odd weekend at a respite care centre to give her daughter a break.'

Here are some other positive steps to take:

● Examine your own motives. Some carers are so proud of their own skills they actually don't want anyone else taking over, but the older person's complete dependence on the carer can lead to guilt and manipulation.

- Take the risk of going out and leaving the older person, either alone for a while, if this is safe, or in the care of someone else. This may not be popular at first but in the end there will be benefits all round.
- Learn to differentiate between real *need* and manipulation. One carer uses her own strategies: before going out she puts the clock back an hour or so, then she can stay out a little longer without her mother worrying.
- Communicate clearly, building up your own strength and resources. The more you respect your own needs, remaining kind but firm, the easier it becomes.
- Remind yourself there is no need for guilt. You are doing a hard but essential task and should feel proud of the achievement.

Finding an identity

Because of the nature of caring, it is very easy for carers to lose sight of their own identity and their rights as individuals. This in turn can lead to depression and then to more sacrifices and feelings of isolation.

Some carers may never have had a very strong sense of themselves. Many women will have moved straight from being the child of their parents to being wife to husband, mother to children, and then carer to a dependant. They have never had the time or opportunity to find out who they really are. Though to some carers this might not seem the ideal time to start to find out, it may be essential if they are to keep going at all. By establishing your own identity and realizing your own needs you have something outside the caring role to hang on to. Often the most helpful way to start exploring these needs and finding answers to them is within a support group. Others can give carers the strength to do things that otherwise they might not feel they had the right to try. As Kathy Weir says:

'First you have to recognize what your own needs are. When you are exhausted and constantly involved in routine tasks of the day, you may not have enough physical and emotional energy to realize. A group helps you explore what you want – then do something about it. One woman in our group whose husband had multiple sclerosis started to learn dancing. One man took a course in writing, another learned pottery, another learned to drive. These were all long-held but unrealized ambitions. One carer had always been very keen on steam trains, so he decided to find time to take up this interest again. He got books out of the library and went on outings. It doesn't really matter what the interest is as long as you can find your own space and pleasure with no commitments to someone else.

'Again, you may have to take a risk and leave the older person for a time. There will be worries – "Will he have a heart attack while I'm gone?", "Will she fall down stairs?", but this could happen whether the carer is there or not.'

Taking action will have three main benefits:

- It gives you, the carer, a break so that you feel stronger, happier, more able to cope.
- This then overlaps onto the cared for who will benefit from your increased peace of mind.
- It will build up resources to deal better with life alone if and when this time comes.

Not that it's always necessary to go out to gain this sense of identity and separateness. One carer who spent a great deal of time with her bedridden mother bought a knitting machine and found that planning and working on the intricate designs helped pass the time pleasantly and profitably. Joyce, who cared for several of her relatives over many years, emphasizes the help that friends can provide and, in her case, the companionship of local church members:

'Even if housebound, it's important for the carers to maintain a certain amount of their own life. A circle of friends can communicate through the telephone, have conversations (not involving the patients' needs) and be involved in the goings on of the outside world, on their own level.

'My church friends were the means of holding me together during a period of isolation. When I could not go to them they came to me and we would have short Bible studies or knitting groups in an upstairs room while keeping a listening ear for my mother's bell, my father's call or my aunt's yell !

'Their availability meant more than anything at times of severe illness. It was worth more than gold to know that I could ring a friend in the middle of the night if I needed to do so, rather than to have people about the house at such sensitive times – and those who were prepared to use their cars should you need a lift to get medicines or a loaf of bread.'

Coping with stress

It also helps to work towards a generally more relaxed attitude to life when coping with the inevitable stresses that are part and parcel of looking after someone else who is disabled, mentally or physically.

Many of the tensions that arise may involve other members of the family. There may be problems because children or partner resent the presence of the older person in the home. Particularly when there is mental confusion, they may find the resulting behaviour embarrassing and offensive. A husband or wife may suffer great stress because of the loss of a sexual relationship with the partner. The warmth and release of physical contact is a great comfort to couples, and its absence can be very hard to bear.

Learning various relaxation techniques not only calms mind and body, but helps untense muscles that are often under great strain from lifting and supporting and can be of great benefit in getting adequate rest and sleep. As mentioned previously, Christine Darby in her book *Keeping Fit While Caring* (Family Welfare Association, 1984) gives several suggestions for exercises that carers can do on their own, either in the morning, late at night or some other time when they can remain quiet and undisturbed. For instance, breathing in and out slowly while counting to ten, or concentrating the mind on one particular thing like birdsong or music can 'stop the anxieties chasing round and round your head', as she puts it.

It is possible to buy relaxation tapes to play (see page 157) and to attend relaxation classes. Your GP, local community centre or Health Education Unit might be able to recommend one. There are also useful books on the subject.

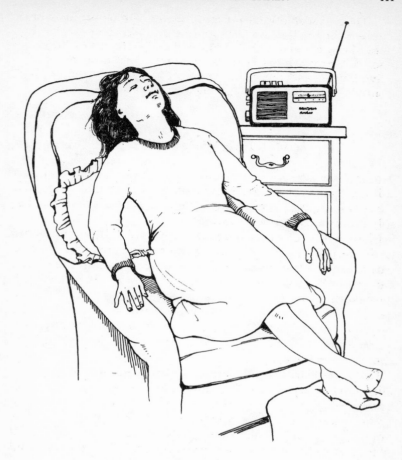

Another helpful method for learning relaxation of both mind and body is yoga. The physical movements keep the body supple, toning up muscles, while each posture encourages mental control. The British Wheel of Yoga and Friends of Yoga are two organizations that can give more details.

The Alexander Technique is a method that corrects faulty physical habits, such as bad posture and over-tense muscles, and also teaches a change in patterns of behaviour and thought so that they become more positive. The Society of

Teachers of the Alexander Technique has a directory of recognized teachers.

Learning assertion

Many carers might find a course in assertiveness training helpful. To carry out much of what has been discussed in this chapter it is necessary to become more assertive. This doesn't mean being manipulative, bossy, selfish or aggressive and turning every discussion into an argument. Nor does it mean being a passive doormat, accepting everything everyone wants of us and never putting our point of view forward. Assertion means realizing what your rights, needs and true feelings are and expressing them clearly and confidently while at the same time respecting the rights of others. In assertiveness training groups, discussions and exercises show how this can be done.

There are a few basic rules for being assertive:

- Decide what you want.
- Decide if it is fair.
- Ask clearly for it.
- Don't be afraid of taking risks.
- Don't bottle up feelings.

All of this seems excellent advice for carers. While maintaining loving care of an older person, you can nevertheless look after yourself and retain a healthy concern for your own interests. Assertiveness training classes are not available at all local community or women's centres, so a useful self-help guide to study is *Assert Yourself* by Gail Lindenfield (Thorsons Publishing Group, 1987.) The Open University also has a leaflet about assertiveness as part of its Community Education Course (for their address see page 154.)

Living with loss

Another reason why it is so important for carers to build up their own outside interests, friendships, strengths and individuality is because an inevitable part of their situation is the probable loss of the older person they are caring for. Again, there is enormous confusion of feelings over this. There are times when carers find themselves longing for the day when they will be free of these hour-by-hour responsibilities. At the same time they will feel guilty for having such thoughts, however fleeting. They will also find that when there *is* release, either because the older person has to go into a residential home or hospital or because of death, they experience great loneliness and loss. The longer the carer has looked after the person the more acute the feelings are of being in a void and of life having lost its meaning. The loss, after all, is a double one – not only of someone dear and close, but of a way of life. The situation can be particularly hard for the carer who is a single person and may have given up home and job to care for an older person. A husband or wife may also suffer acute loneliness and distress when there is no wider family to turn to. A single woman in her sixties says:

> 'Even if the other person has been difficult, one feels a great sense of loss after the death. I think there should be far more help over this. People seem to think you're delighted it's over and expect you to plunge into life again, but I know from others that there is a long period of adjustment.
>
> 'I'm aware many carers have a home life and families at my age. I have none because when I was free most of the men were married. Any woman alone, even widows, find couples are reluctant to share their friendship.'

Says another carer, 'Now I am alone and am 59 years old, with another year to wait for my retirement pension.' 'I am a Cinderella with no hopes of any Prince Charming,' says another.

These are sad situations, and perhaps a warning to other carers not to put *all* their eggs in one basket and take care of themselves physically, mentally and, if possible, financially. But however hard you try to keep your own interests and identity you are bound to suffer the same shock of bereavement that everyone does after the loss of a loved one.

Joyce, a carer, feels that much of the advice that applies

before bereavement is equally useful afterwards because this can be another period of isolation, only of another kind. She passes on the following positive suggestions:

- **Continuity**
  There needs to be a continuity somewhere to allow life to go on. That is where friends are so important – with the same friends one can continue the knitting groups, the chats or whatever.

- **Time**
  This is a big factor. Nothing in nature can be hurried and bereavement is a process, like a tunnel, that you must go through and cannot escape, but it takes time.

- **Stages**
  Although people react in different ways, we all go through stages of bereavement – crying, wanting to be alone, wanting to be needed, wanting company, wanting to run home as soon as we get out. Acceptance is half the battle and helps us resist guilt feelings, regrets, resentments.

- **New habits**
  Eventually we find a different reason for doing the same things we did before – there is now no need to put the light on so that mother can see the way to her chair but so that you can read a letter!

- **Loneliness**
  Maybe the hardest times are to eat alone and notice the empty chair. Why not choose your favourite programme, write a letter, read a book and eat your meal with a different object in view?

- **Being yourself**
  Allow periods of time to be yourself – relax, mope, laugh, be alone. Also spoil yourself and treat yourself to some of the things you like doing. Eventually your whole life can be remoulded and fit the person you really are.

- **Make changes**
  One of the hardest and most emotional stages of bereavement is thinking about past associations – the empty chair, seeing furniture as obstacles. Take time to gradually re-create one room, then another, putting *yourself* into it instead of the other person. Do things you were never free

to do before, such as entertaining, and the place will be refilled and life will come into the home again.

Remember too that there are various voluntary organizations specializing in the support and counselling of the bereaved, such as CRUSE (one of their members will see any bereaved person whether a relative or a friend) and the National Association of Widows. It's at this time that a carers' support group can be of great help as well. Kathy Weir describes how several of their members suffered a bereavement, and each time it was extremely sad and very moving for them all:

> 'Because this has happened, or will happen to all of the group, the sympathy has been real and deeply felt. Each time I've been touched by the feeling that somehow, despite the great sense of grief and loss, the death has been part of life and each person has been consoled by the thought of how care and concern eased the relative or friend's life and death.'

CHAPTER 7
The cost of caring

'We're poor and problems arise every time my mother needs to attend doctor's surgery or hospital. It is a nightmare getting her anywhere because her legs are so painful. We have to pay for taxis out of mum's basic pension.'

'I did what I could to help my neighbours because their relations didn't want to know. I did get the attendance allowance for them, but no way would they part with it to pay me for helping.'

Caring is a very costly business, financially as well as emotionally. Day-to-day living expenses can be hard enough to cover without the added bills from extra heating, special foods, increased laundry and washing, home adaptations, transport and so on.

As we've already seen, many carers have to give up full or part-time jobs to look after someone at home. They often have to scrape together an income and are desperately in need of any extra financial assistance that is available.

Mavis is a carer who never married and devoted many years of her life to looking after her parents, both of whom lived into their nineties and needed a great deal of attention:

'I started nursing my mother when she was 82-years-old. She was still able to get around, but I was doing a full-time job and keeping the house going, doing washing, cooking, shopping, etc. Then my mother was taken ill. She became incontinent and remained like that for four long years, sleeping downstairs. The doctor informed me I must give up my job to nurse her. I was then 58 and my job was kept open for six months without pay, after which I was without financial assistance for another year.

'Dad had to keep me, which he resented. After a second application mum got Attendance Allowance and the situation was eased somewhat, but during the 18 months before retiring age I had to spend my post office savings to keep myself solvent.'

After Mavis' mother died, her father became ill. He, too, was granted an Attendance Allowance, again after a second application, but he did not allow her to use it. Instead he would put it straight in the bank. 'For the last four years of his life before he died aged 96 I was expected to keep house on £10 per week. He was responsible only for rates and insurance. That was a few years ago now, but it was very difficult.' The final twist for this carer was that when her father died her sisters, who had done very little to help look after him, benefitted equally under the will, even inheriting some of the banked Attendance Allowance!

However, the story does have a happy ending. Because she had been prepared to stay at home and do the caring, eventually her mother's sister left her a sum of money in her will and she bought a small flat. Now in her seventies she is able to enjoy her life and, in spite of the money problems, has some very affectionate memories of her parents.

Common difficulties

This carer's experiences highlight some common difficulties. Above all, many simply do not realize in the first place that welfare benefits and financial assistance of other sorts exist. On the whole, it is not the habit of the DHSS to inform people in any particular situation (whether they be unemployed, single parents or carers) that there is cash help available. Instead we are expected to find out for ourselves, but to do this we really need some idea at the start that there is something to be eligible for. The end result of this catch-22 predicament is that carers, like thousands of other members of the general public, are going without benefits, grants and other financial assistance they could be claiming. It has been shown that, even though carers save the government billions of pounds by looking after elderly people at home, they are losing out themselves on millions of pounds in unclaimed benefits.

The various carers' associations, support groups and publications aimed at carers are helping by spelling out very clearly what is actually available, but this means carers being in the right place or reading the right publication at the right time, and many are too busy or too tired to make such efforts. As Mavis' experience shows, there can also be other problems with which to contend:

- Some older people who are receiving Attendance Allowance do not make it available for general household expenses.
- Others do not want to claim this or other benefits because they see it as charity.
- To qualify for Invalid Care Allowance, a benefit paid direct to the carer, the older person must be receiving Attendance Allowance.
- First claims are often turned down, and then it is necessary to make a second application.

It is easy to see why some of these difficulties arise. For some older people, the Attendance Allowance, plus their Income Support and/or pension, is the only money they can call their own, and it gives them a feeling of independence and even status. But if the household income is low, they have to be persuaded that, even though it is their right to use the money as they see fit, they should contribute to the costs of being looked after. Some use the money to pay for extra help in the home, for instance, or for special expenses such as foods for a diet, washing powder, or payments on a new washing machine.

It's also understandable that older people who have grown up in a different era may feel that asking for welfare benefits smacks of begging or the workhouse. They see receiving the money as something to be ashamed of, not as a right. But cash support in their situation *is* a right. Carers and their dependants will have paid income tax, national insurance, rates and so on over the years and now it is their turn to reap the benefits. On top of this, carers are doing a job that deserves payment.

Proving their case

Unfortunately, having persuaded the elderly person that the money is theirs by right, carers and their dependants may then find that they have to *prove* these rights to the DHSS. Claiming benefits does involve a great deal of form filling, assessment of income and examination of the needs of both carer and the elderly person. So it's not surprising that many give up at this stage. If you are not very confident in the first place, you are going to feel even less happy when being closely questioned about exactly how many hours caring is needed, what this involves, what your income and expenses are, down to the last pound, to what degree the older person is disabled, how much they have in savings and so on. If, having gone through all this, the benefits are witheld, it is only the very brave and determined who are going to appeal. Even though Judith Oliver would like to see all carers and their dependants doing this, she understands only too well their reluctance:

'It's easier to get money for people who are dying than for those who are surviving for a long period. It is simpler to get a lump sum from a grant-giving body for a person who is terminally ill than Attendance Allowance or Invalid Care Allowance over a length of time.

'Benefits are totally inadequate for long-term illness and disability anyway. As things stand at the moment they don't allow people to have a reasonable life. Many carers live at poverty level and can't even afford to feed themselves properly. Sick people need more than £30 a week to live on. Most of us would need more than that to keep us warm during a bout of 'flu. Nor should the carer's benefit be dependent on the older person receiving Attendance Allowance. If mother says she won't live off charity or won't allow the DHSS to look into her financial situation, as things stand, there is very little the carer can do about it.'

However, putting pressure on the authorities can bring about change, as was proved by the example of Mrs Jacqueline Drake who took her case to the European Court of Human Rights and won, benefiting other carers at the same time. Before this, like other married or cohabiting women,

Jacqueline had not been eligible for Invalid Care Allowance, even though she had given up her job to care for her dependant elderly mother who was receiving Attendance Allowance. Jacqueline was considered to be supported by her husband and therefore not in need of benefit. *Men* who gave up a job to care for a dependant at home, did receive Invalid Care Allowance, whether or not they had a partner. By proving that under the Bill of Equal Rights this was sexual discrimination, Jacqueline Drake won Invalid Care Allowance for all women under retiring age.

Looking ahead

The hope is that, with an increasing awareness of what caring for an older person at home can involve, plus more pressure from carers and their supporters, there will be many such improvements. In the meantime it is essential for family and friends to take a careful look at income and expenditure and work out ways of dealing with them. For instance:

- **Sharing bills**
  Total up all the living expenses, including accommodation, rates, rent, repairs, insurance, gas, electricity, water, telephone, food, TV licence and rental and so on and decide what is a fair and possible contribution from the older person's income. If discussed together right at the start, there is less likely to be friction and disagreement later on.
- **Seek advice**
  Before sharing a house, a younger family and/or older person may be receiving some form of benefit, such as Income Support or help with rent and rates. These may be affected by sharing a house, so check this out with your local Citizen's Advice Bureau or at the DHSS office.
- **Pension protection**
  Carers must safeguard their own futures and think of the time they may be left on their own again. Home Responsibilities Protection preserves the pension rights of those who are not paying National Insurance contributions

because they are looking after someone at home. This includes married women who give up work to care for a severely disabled person (ask at your local Employment or DHSS office about this).

Finally check out *all* the benefits and other forms of financial help for which you may be eligible. 'If in doubt, *claim*,' is the best advice because many people could receive much more than they realize. Some of these benefits may appear small in themselves, but added together they can make a great deal of difference to coping with the day-to-day and week-by-week costs of caring.

Welfare benefits

Because of government changes, particularly under the new Social Security Act, amounts and types of benefit have altered. However, at the time of writing, the following are the main benefits available to carers and their dependants:

- **Attendance Allowance**
  This is paid direct to the dependant and is for severely disabled people, with rates varying according to need. There is a higher rate if care is needed day and night and a lower rate if it is needed only during the day or only at night. It is tax free, not subject to income or National Insurance contributions, and available from the DHSS. A letter from GP, hospital, social worker, day centre worker, health visitor or any other involved professional in support of your application is helpful. This is dealt with by an independent Attendance Allowance board, and a doctor will examine the dependant person. Remember, a second application can be made if the person is refused.
- **Invalid Care Allowance**
  This is a cash benefit payable to carers who cannot work because they are looking after a dependant person. It is necessary to show that you spend 35 hours a week caring for the person and do not earn more than a certain set limit. However, you cannot claim Invalid Care Allowance for the first time after you have reached pensionable age and the

dependant should be receiving Attendance Allowance.
Also, if you are receiving Income Support (formerly called
Supplementary Benefit) you may not find it pays to receive
Invalid Care Allowance as Income Support would auto-
matically be reduced.

● **Income Support**
Those on a low income or over retirement age can apply
for Income Support to top up their earnings or pension.
Through the new Social Fund it may also be possible to
claim loans or grants to pay for extra costs or to help in a
sudden crisis. The Social Fund replaces the Single Payments that used to be available in these situations. A letter
from your GP or some other involved professionals helps
when making claims.

● **Mobility Allowance**
This is a weekly benefit paid to those who are unable, or
virtually unable, to walk because of physical disablement
and are likely to remain so for at least a year. This could
mean that the dependant is confined to bed or that walking
would endanger life or health, for instance after a stroke, or
that walking ability is very restricted and painful. The
money can then be spent to help on transport costs. The
older person must have been in this situation for at least a
year and must be under 66 when the claim is first made.
After this birthday it is payable until the age of 75. When
claiming, ask the GP or hospital specialist to include
evidence that there are valid difficulties in getting
around.

● **Severe Disablement Allowance**
Those who are over retirement age and are receiving a
pension that is lower than the Severe Disablement
Allowance and are also assessed as 80 per cent disabled,
may be able to receive this benefit instead. Anyone receiving Attendance Allowance, a war disablement pension or
who is registered blind or partially sighted, would qualify,
but since it is difficult to assess the degree of disablement of
each individual, seek advice from your GP, a hospital
specialist or social worker or ask at the DHSS office for
more details.

- **Housing Benefit**
This is for those paying rent and rates on a low income. You may be able to get more help because there is a disabled person in the house or someone older needing special care. Nor will you be expected to pay rates on facilities needed because of disability such as an extra bathroom or toilet, garage or parking space.

- **Transport benefits**
Apart from the Mobility Allowance there is other help available for disabled people. For instance, if a car is regularly used to transport them about, then this may be eligible for exemption from road tax (Vehicle Excise Duty.) There are also parking concessions when a passenger has severe mobility problems (including blind people) so that you can park nearer shops, buildings and other places being visited. This is called the Orange Badge Scheme. The Motability Scheme helps people with disabilities who want to use their Mobility Allowance to buy or rent a car or wheelchair and gives advice on how to do this. There are also special concessions available on prices and a Mobility Information Service that gives advice on which vehicles suit which types of disability. (For address, see page 154.) Finally, British Rail makes special travel concessions for those receiving Mobility or Attendance Allowance.

- **Health Benefits**
Don't forget, too, that those over pensionable age are eligible for a whole range of benefits from the National Health Service. These may include free prescriptions for medicines, surgical appliances and nursing equipment, hearing aids, dental treatment, eye tests and glasses, chiropody, wheelchairs and many other aids, such as walking frames and incontinence pants and pads. Hospital fares may also be refunded.

- **Family Credit**
If you have children and are working at least 24 hours per week as well as caring, you may be able to claim this benefit, which is means tested. This could be very helpful if you are looking after a disabled older person for under 35 hours a week and are, therefore, not entitled to Invalid Care Allowance.

Bear in mind that if an older person goes into hospital or a residential home for a period of time this may mean a change in the benefits, even if it is only a temporary one. Attendance Allowance and Invalid Care Allowance could be stopped, for instance, and the pension would automatically be transferred to pay towards the cost of professional care.

Details of all the benefits mentioned here are given in separate DHSS leaflets available from the Post Office, and each has its own claim form. There is also a helpful publication from Age Concern called *Your Rights for Pensioners*. The Disability Alliance or one of the organizations giving specialist support to carers, such as the Carers National Association can give up-to-date information on recent changes.

Tax and grants

There are now, regretfully, no useful tax concessions for people looking after an elderly dependant person. However, as already described, there are grants available through the local authority housing and social services departments to cover adaptations to the house. These include hand rails, ramps, home insulation and installing an extra shower and toilet.

Other grants are available from various voluntary organizations and charities if the older person and the carer are living in very poor circumstances and simply can't get by. As well as advising on all financial assistance available to older people and those who look after them, Counsel and Care for the Elderly (CCE) also makes its own cash grants available to those in special need. Generally the older person must still be living in his or her own home and have less than £2,000 in savings. If the money is used to pay towards extra help, such as day or night nursing or a care attendant, then the older person is expected to contribute. Application forms are available from CCE, plus advice on other sources of grant aid.

Legal matters

If an older person's affairs are at all complicated and he or she owns a business or house, it is best to get legal advice when caring first begins. For instance if he or she eventually becomes incapable of dealing with financial matters, there are two ways in which others can take over:

- **Power of Attorney**
  This gives one person legal rights over another person's affairs. It can only be granted when the one creating the Power of Attorney is found to be mentally capable, so unfortunately it is too late once senile dementia has progressed beyond a certain point. It is therefore a very sensible practice for older people to think about this themselves earlier on and choose someone to handle their affairs whom they trust and who is close to them.

- **The Court of Protection**
  The court can appoint someone, such as a solicitor or a member of the family, to take over a person's affairs if that person has become mentally incapable. The person appointed is called a receiver, and must be supervised by the court to prevent fraud. A fee, based on the income of the person whose affairs are being handled, is charged and this can be costly, so ask about charges before going ahead.

When sharing their home with an elderly person, some families and friends take the step of drawing up a contract with the help of a solicitor so that agreements about the arrangement are legally covered. To some this may appear rather calculated and cold-hearted, but, particularly when there are shared finances, loans made or a joint mortgage taken out, a legal contract safeguards the interests of the older people as well as those caring for them. Whatever the arrangements are when sharing starts, situations and relationships can change. There might be a marriage break-up, unemployment, the need to move house or simply strains between older and younger generation that make it impossible to continue. Disablement or mental frailty may make it necessary for older people to go into residential care, or lead them to make illogical and unreasonable accusations. If the older person has put money into the home or it is owned jointly and there is a need for change, then this could lead to all sorts of complications. A house owned solely by an elderly person receiving long-term residential care might even have to be sold. If a legal arrangement is made right at the beginning about what to do there will be great savings for everyone both financially and emotionally.

A common answer is to have what is called a Private Trust Agreement drawn up by a solicitor and signed by each person concerned. This can be tailor-made to each family's requirements, but should certainly cover financial arrangements and what will happen if and when sharing comes to an end. If there is a joint mortgage and one person stops paying his or her share, then the lender will insist that the responsibility for the debt is taken on by the remaining borrowers jointly and severally. This means that each person is liable not just for their part, but all payments. It is sad but realistic advice that you must also take into account what will happen when older people die. You can take out insurance to protect you in the case of joint ownership in a mortgage agreement, and it is also very important that everyone involved makes out a proper will, younger as well as older.

For general legal advice, go to your solicitor or to your local Citizen's Advice Bureau or Neighbourhood Law Centre which should be able to offer free advice and helpful leaflets. Though it may be difficult to do, also try to involve older relatives or friends at an early stage so that they, too, can make their wishes known. When my widowed father was growing older it was *he* who told me where to find his various important papers, such as tax details, bank statements, will and so on, if he should be taken suddenly ill. At the time he looked so well and life seemed so ordinary and happy on that sunny Saturday afternoon that I found it painful, almost embarrassing, to talk about such things, but a few years later when he was very ill and eventually died, I was very grateful to him for his courage and foresight in taking this initiative.

CHAPTER 8
Finding more help

'If I could ring up the services and say can I have them when I need them, it would be lovely. But you're in their hands as regards time. Also, my husband doesn't like strangers. It just wouldn't be worth the row.'

'My mother sees little and is registered partially sighted, but as she is not yet totally blind no social worker calls to have a friendly chat with her.'

On the face of it there seems to be a lot of help available for carers in the form of care attendant schemes, community nursing teams, day centres run by social services and support from voluntary organisations. Yet when you actually talk to carers there are a huge number who have great difficulty in finding and getting this help and they struggle on alone. In one survey carried out by the Association of Carers, 83 per cent of those looking after a disabled dependant said they received no assistance whatsover from anyone else.

Judith Oliver, founder of the Association, thinks there are a variety of reasons for this situation. Above all she has found that carers often simply do not know that help exists. Even when they do know in theory, they may find that in practice their particular area does not provide much in the way of services. She adds that carers also experience the following problems:

- If an elderly person has a carer then help is less likely to be offered.
- If the carer, rather than the elderly person, asks for assistance, then help is less likely to be given.

- The more dependent and frail the older person is, the less suitable help is available.
- Many of the services aren't appropriate to the carers' needs anyway.

'So often it is the cared for that help is aimed at, not the carers. For instance, most don't need a home help to clean and wash-up. They want a district nurse to help get the older person up at 7.30 in the morning or to help get them to bed at night. Sometimes such nursing help is available, but not at the times needed. Frequently when carers do ask for help it is refused. When they apply they don't get it because they live in the wrong area, because dependants are too disabled to qualify or they are in the wrong age group. For instance, one husband of 63 who had a stroke couldn't go to the stroke club because he was under retirement age.'

The Association has also found that the very tasks with which carers desperately need help from professionals, such as bathing, are often not seen as part of the job of the community nursing team. This can create a number of difficulties.

One of the added strains of caring is that it is often necessary to push down very natural emotions in order to undertake certain intimate and personal tasks, such as deal-ing with soiling through incontinence. Taboos are strong over personal uncleanliness and intimate cross sex touching and the experience of a lot of carers is that they can only do these things by professionalizing them and pretending, for instance, that they are nurses. But having to override natural reactions complicates their other feelings of love and close-ness. To have professional help with such tasks would make caring a lot easier and could help many carers and their families feel more emotionally stable and secure.

Refusing help

Another difficulty is that dependant older people may refuse help that is offered. They do not like someone else, however expert, looking after them. They may refuse to go to a Day Centre or to a hospital as part of a hospital respite scheme. Many carers reach a stage where, even when help is available, they feel it isn't worth the battle and they may just as well manage on their own. Judith Oliver comments that:

> 'As we know, caring is a common cause of depression. When people are depressed they aren't likely to wake up and think, "Right, today I'll go and find some help." They are more likely to give up. In fact, they are often in such a state they can't stand the hassle of having someone else in the house – tidying up before the helper arrives, being in at the right time, waiting for transport. They can't take the extra strain.'

One hospital social worker was so concerned by the plight of the carers she met during the course of her work that she decided to become a counsellor and now runs a support group so that she can devote time to their needs at a more personal level.

> 'There are facilities, but people don't know about them or can't take advantage of them. I've met people who could have had help from a volunteer, from a care attendant scheme like Crossroads, from a hospital social worker like myself, but they weren't told how or where to find these people. "If only we had known – why didn't anyone tell us?", people who come to the support group ask. If you have a child who is even mildly handicapped you know right from the start that there are people there to help, but when you are caring for an older person you seem to be left to fend for yourself.'

Using what's available

Through her support groups this counsellor is helping carers to find out what services are available in their area and how to make full use of them:

> 'Many carers are very proud, and with reason. They are usually the experts and they know how to do their job. On the other hand, they do get tired and depressed and have the feeling there is no end to it. They want help, but it's got to be of the right quality and type.
> 'They may also find it difficult to stand up to a relative who refuses help, whether financial or practical. By talking over these problems together in the group or through one-to-one counselling they find ways of dealing with this.'

Such techniques have already been discussed in earlier chapters. Learning to be more assertive, for instance, is very important. So is a refusing to feel guilty or be manipulated – insist quietly but firmly instead that, even though the older person may not like it at first, it is essential for there to be extra support. It's also necessary to do this early, before the wear and tear of coping alone over a long period wears carers down. If you have entered into the vicious circle of isolation/ resentment/depression already described, it becomes increasingly difficult to demand the help that is needed.

It may also be necessary to bring in a third party who can mediate between carer and cared for if the dependant person is refusing help. This might be another relative or friend or a professional, such as a health visitor or GP. One carer describes her experience:

> 'After my husband had a stroke he became very dependant on me. However, I really needed a break and I also thought it would help my husband to go to a day centre sometimes for the stimulation of outside activities and other people. But when the transport arrived he used to stand on the doorstep and make the most awful scenes until I had to give in. I couldn't bear the neighbours hearing the noise. It made me feel I was being cruel to him.'

Eventually the situation was sorted out by their GP. He came in and talked to the husband, explaining to him that if his wife was going to be able to go on caring for him at home, then she must have the occasional break. Her husband then agreed to go peacefully and, in fact, found he enjoyed the outings once he had become used to the new surroundings. On top of this, speech therapy and occupational therapy available at the centre helped him recover much of his speech and mobility. He was therefore less dependant on his wife when he was at home.

Sources of information

At a national level there are various ways of finding out what types of services exist for carers and their dependants. One excellent source is the Carer's National Association (formerly the Association of Carers and the National Council for Carers and their Elderly Dependants but now combined under one umbrella). The National Association has booklets, leaflets and regular newsletters with information updates on benefits, care attendant schemes and professional services.

Age Concern and Help the Aged, the two main organizations supporting older people, also have helpful information. The latter has a hot line which you can ring for specific advice, and both have literature on many aspects of caring. Age Concern produces a listing of home help and day care services around the country. These range from a Coventry scheme providing residential home helps who live in during a crisis, to a night-sitting service in Norfolk.

Excellent though the schemes described in this Age Concern directory are, they serve as examples of good practice rather than giving an accurate picture of services all over the country. What is also needed is easy access to information about *local* services for carers everywhere. North Yorkshire social services department, for instance, produce their own comprehensive directory, listing all the benefits, aids, local support schemes and professional services, where to go for them and how to get them. The directory also lists the names and addresses of local branches of national organizations as well as locally-based groups. It would be wonderful if every local authority in the country were to do the same so that, as soon as caring for an elderly relative at home begins, all those looking after them have instant knowledge of where to go for help rather than having to find out for themselves.

Home and away

There are two fundamental types of support for carers. There are the teams of people who come *into* the home – health visitors, community nurses and domiciliary helps – and there are the facilities *outside* the home – where older people can go so that the carer has a break. Ideally these services, whether provided by professionals or volunteers, should work together and there should be an equal partnership between the paid professional helpers and the home-based carers. In Chapter 2

Government and local authority help available to carers

National Health Service

Hospital
Geriatrician
Neurologist
Psycho-geriatrician
Nurses
Physiotherapy
Occupational therapy
Speech therapy
Continence adviser
Medical social worker
Dietician
Community nursing

Community health authority
Community nursing
Health visitors
Home physiotherapy
Home speech therapy
Community psychiatric nursing
Chiropodists
Dental, eye and ear care
Other health benefits, such as
free prescriptions, hospital
aids and travel costs

Social Services
Social workers
Home helps
Meals on wheels
Transport
Day centres
Respite care
Occupational therapists
Grants for home aids and
adaptations

DHSS
Income Support
Family Credit
Attendance Allowance
Invalid Care Allowance
Mobility Allowance
Severe Disability Allowance
Housing Benefit

the various sources of help from social, health and hospital services are listed. The diagram above gives a brief summary of the roles of the various workers. The following are further sources of support provided outside the home:

● **Day Centres**
These are often attached to residential homes and are run by the social services department for the relatively active older people. Day Care Centres are for those who are more disabled and frail, but both types should provide activities, meals and transport to get to the centre and home again. Demand is high and places limited, so most older people attend one or two days a week. Local authorities and

voluntary organizations also run luncheon clubs and drop-in centres that older people can attend for a midday meal and social activities.

● **Short-term care**

In certain areas it is possible for older people to stay in the hospital or residential home on a short-term basis. This is called 'respite care', because it gives the carer a 'respite'. This may be for a night, for a couple of days or weekend, or for a week or longer so that the carer can have a holiday. Contact your GP, social services department, community health department or your local branch of Age Concern to find out what respite care is available in your area.

● **Fostering**

In some parts of the country there are foster schemes that operate in a way similar to child fostering, but it is the older person who goes to stay in the home of a trained person for a short period of time. Those fostering have often spent time looking after their own elderly relatives or friends and are experienced in coping with their needs. They will often take older people on a regular basis so that they become familiar with the foster family and settled in this second home. Contact Age Concern, who have monitored schemes in Liverpool, Leeds and Leicestershire, to see if anything similar exists in your area.

Private care

With the present shortage in local authority services, many carers are turning to private schemes for help. There are now several hundred registered employment agencies providing nursing and domestic help in England and Wales. These can be especially helpful on a short-term basis when an older person at home is seriously ill or disabled and the carer is desperately in need of assistance or back-up relief. Some agencies can provide highly qualified nurses who will give expert care day and night. Others may supply trained care attendants who can come in as day or night-sitters and share some of the tasks that need to be done or give the carer some time off.

There are two main pitfalls to watch out for when using private care. The first is obviously cost. Fees can be high and completely beyond the means of carer and cared for who may already be existing on a very low income. Some families use Attendance Allowance or Invalid Care Allowance to pay for this help. When there is nothing else available and there is a real need for skilled support, local authorities may contribute towards the cost, so it is worth contacting the local social services department about this. Also some charitable organizations give special grants (see page 124).

Another consideration with private care is value for money. Some agencies are excellent and give a high standard of service while others are more suspect, particularly if older people are living in their own homes and there is no one else there to regularly supervise what is happening. There are the 'cowboys' of home care just as there are cowboy builders and plumbers.

Personal recommendations, or an agency like GRACE, which gives guidance on private residential homes and private sources of domestic care, will help you avoid such people. The social services department may be able to advise and already have contacts with local agencies. Age Concern produces a useful booklet that you might find helpful.

The Centre for Policy on Ageing has surveyed the standard of private care and suggests that a written contract is drawn up when someone is employed, stating duties and the fee agreed. The carer and the older person then have some come-back if the private care is not all it promised to be.

Voluntary schemes

The other main source of help to carers is, yet again, provided by the various voluntary organizations who run care attendant schemes. Some of the attendants are volunteers, some are paid staff, but all are trained to help the carer within the home by sitting with the older person or assisting with nursing and domestic tasks normally undertaken by the carer.

Crossroads is the biggest such scheme, with 120 branches in various parts of the country and more to come. The service is free to the carer as Crossroads schemes are mainly funded by the DHSS, local authorities and other funding bodies. A member of Crossroads comments that:

> 'It is perhaps surprising that with district nurses, health visitors, social workers, occupational therapists, home helps, Meals on Wheels and so on, there should be an unmet need, but there is. Without in any way duplicating the help provided by any of these services, a properly trained, reliable care attendant can be the crucial factor in determining whether or not a disabled person is able to go on living at home.'

The Crossroads head office (for their address, see page 147) can put you in touch with the branch nearest to you. Your GP, social services department or a local umbrella organization for disabled people may also know of care attendant schemes in your area, including any run by the local authority. Some of these are neighbourhood projects, with the social services department training and paying neighbours to take part in looking after local elderly people.

The Family Welfare Association in London and other voluntary organizations such as those for the disabled also run care attendant schemes. Sometimes these are very much a local initiative, as, for instance, the home hospice project covering a very rural part of Norfolk. This group trains volunteers to support older people who are terminally ill in their own homes.

The Women's Royal Voluntary Service (WRVS) have a 'home from hospital' service. This is offered for a 48-hour period after a patient is discharged from hospital if there is no one at home to receive them. The WRVS provides support until friends or relatives can take over. The WRVS also has a 'good neighbour' scheme, providing meals and domestic help, and Books on Wheels, which delivers books to elderly people unable to visit libraries.

Shortage of transport

However much there may be in the way of help and activities

outside the home, a major difficulty for many carers and their elderly dependants is shortage of transport. When they have no car, even a short trip to the shops, day centre or hospital becomes a nightmare if they are trying to use trains and buses. It is for this reason that so many become virtually tied to their homes and isolated from the world outside.

Again the WRVS is an important source of help. This organization has local transport schemes that can provide transport for essential visits to people like your GP or chiropodist and, perhaps, for other outings, but authorization that there is a real need for this type of transport has to come from a doctor, hospital or social services department. Social services will themselves provide transport to take older people to day centres, for instance, and the health service provide door-to-door transport by ambulance when hospital visits or treatment are necessary. There are also voluntary schemes in various areas where volunteers offer lifts in their own cars and you may be able to find out about this through a local Age Concern branch, Volunteer Bureau or Council for Voluntary Service (CVS). As already mentioned in earlier chapters, there is a special Mobility Allowance to help with transport costs, and Mobility Advice Centres can give information on adapting vehicles for disabled people. In some circumstances you can also claim for the fares to and from hospital if public transport or taxis are used. Nevertheless, transport remains a problem, especially if it is needed for purely social reasons, such as visiting friends and family or having a pleasant outing in the countryside or some place of interest.

An organization called Contact, which has been running for some years now, recognized this need and formed a network of volunteers with cars who were willing to take older people out on Sunday afternoons and entertain them to tea. Some carers' support groups manage to hire or even buy their own minibuses and cars so carers and older people can, not only get to meetings, but have outings together and help with transport in an emergency.

One London Neighbourhood Project, set up by the local Mental Health Association and Age Concern to form a network of drop-in centres for isolated and confused elderly people in the area, found that the biggest problem was lack of transport to and from their homes. They are now working on improving the local community transport scheme and volunteers not only run the drop-in centres but act as drivers, using vehicles on loan from community centres and other voluntary organizations.

The ethnic minorities

Although every chapter and section in this book applies to *all* carers and their elderly dependants, regardless of their origins or nationality, there are some particular problems experienced by those from what are commonly called the 'ethnic minorities' that need special mention. Many of these problems have escaped attention until fairly recently.

A common myth is that older people whose roots were originally in countries far from this one are more likely to be part of an extended family with support already on hand. As one Liverpool housing association manager points out, even the Chinese family network is breaking down and a lot of elderly Chinese are unable to be supported by their younger ones. The younger members of the family may also live in small houses where there is no room for their elderly relatives.

Another myth is that, because these older people are a minority in this country, their numbers are small, but this is not so. In Liverpool alone there are around 20,000 black people born and bred in the city, plus émigrés totalling 2,000 Somalis and Arabs, 8,000 Chinese and 3,000 people from the Caribbean. Yet here, as elsewhere, their needs are often overlooked.

Many people who emigrated to this country in their middle and later years have not learned the language. A typical example is an elderly Asian couple who do not speak or read any English. The husband has suffered two strokes in the past two years and is paralysed down one side. His wife has been trying to look after him, but she is suffering from nervous strain and stress. No home help had been provided, and it is only since a friend has told them that they are entitled to Attendance and Mobility Allowances that they have made a claim. Other older people have difficulty in hospital making themselves understood or in understanding what is being said to them. One Asian man who was in hospital for five weeks was fed only boiled vegetables because there was no Asian food provided and he could not explain what he wanted to eat. Meals on Wheels do not usually cater for cultural differences in diet.

Some black older people have also complained of racial comments being made to them by home helps and by white staff and residents in homes.

Steps are slowly being taken to improve the situation. In Liverpool, for instance, one project set up small, community-based homes for Somali, Chinese and Caribbean elderly people needing sheltered housing. Campaigning groups are asking that the DHSS provide leaflets explaining welfare benefits and support services in a variety of languages, including Hindi and Urdu. They would also like to see interpreters in hospitals, the employment of home helps who understand cultural differences and Meals on Wheels menus that cater for all dietary needs. Some local authorities and voluntary organizations are setting up multicultural social and luncheon clubs where older people can go and meet each other and find out more about health education and the medical services available locally. Here they can also remember and talk about their shared culture and traditions. One organization that has been set up specifically to campaign on their behalf is the Standing Conference of Ethnic Minority Senior Citizens (SCEMSC) (for their address, see page 147).

Campaigning for change

Many carers, particularly those who join organizations like the Carers' National Association or who attend support groups, eventually become interested in what could be called the 'politics of caring'. Realizing how much is lacking in services, not just for them but for thousands of others, they decide to push for improvements. Isolated in their own homes it is very difficult to make an impression on the authorities, but by joining together carers can speak with a louder voice and really make themselves heard. Kathy Weir of the Family Welfare Association says that:

> 'Two of our group members came with me to a carers' conference run by professional workers. They were fired by what they heard and shared information and ideas with the rest of the group when we got back.
>
> 'Now they have become more involved in campaigning for change in the future. The focus on themselves and their lives has to come first, but a concern for wider issues develops naturally from this more personal base.'

That change and improvements in the caring field are needed she has no doubts. For care in the community to really live up to its name, every city, town and rural area in the country should have its own centre where day and night support is available, plus all the other back-up services that are so essential to carers. Kathy Weir continues:

> 'People should be able to choose whether to be carers or not. What is essential, as the carers themselves are telling us, is that the facilities should be available to make this a *real* choice. It should be easier for a man or woman to work outside the home and be carers, to go out and enjoy themselves and be carers, to study and be carers, to relax and be carers, to have enough money and be carers, to lead their own lives and be carers.'

As I hope this book has shown, there are some wonderful examples of back-up services in certain areas of the country, and the hope is that others will follow their lead. In the meantime the mushrooming carers' support groups are filling some of the gaps and continuing to work towards improvements everywhere.

Let me conclude with the words of one carer who has found new courage and energy she would not have thought possible:

> 'Finding help was the best possible support for me. It's made such a difference to my life that I've started a local group. Social services gave us a hall and we talk about our problems, knowing our relatives are all right. It's given me new energy to look after him and I've found strengths I never knew I had.

'Fancy me getting a group going! It now seems to go by itself, and we've decided to meet in people's homes as we've all become such good friends. Mind you, we're not just talking and having a good laugh – we're telling the social services what we and our relatives want!'

Let's hope that you, the carers, are listened to and that, before too long, you have all you need – and more besides.

A carer's experience

'My wife has dementia. She is 66 and keeps excellent health and is very mobile – but she doesn't know who I am. It started two years ago. She became very forgetful – we've lost three electric kettles when she's put them on the gas – and lagged behind when we were out walking. Then one day she said: "Where've you been? You're the other man, where's my husband?" We went to the doctor and hospitals and had different tests. Over the two years it worsened gradually. She's bright and full of talk, but you can't hold an intelligent conversation with her. She forgets what she's just said. I can't go out on my own for long. I've lost my freedom, that's gone right out of the window. I used to go to judo twice a week but I can't any more. My daughter lives too far away and though we've known the neighbours for years, my wife doesn't want them coming in. She can't explain why, she just gets cross. I have tried to take her to the day centre but when we walked in she smelled cooking and said "I'm not staying here. I'm coming home, they're all old ladies and men." I think her pride is hurt. But if I let her out on her own I've no idea what she'd do. She has no idea of the value of money and she'll call a pound a penny or go back to calling them shillings and pence. We go out together and everywhere we go seems to be a strange place. We do go on holidays and, funnily enough, my wife seems to find her way around better when we're abroad. I think she's stimulated by it. When we're home she says: "You can go out. There's nothing wrong with me." But I'm frightened to leave her. She turns the gas on and forgets to light it. She ironed my trousers and left a great hole in them. She can cook under supervision, but when I try to correct her or show her she says, "I don't need you to tell me." I suppose she's happy enough, she doesn't cry or weep. She seems to be in a little world of her own. She thinks I'm her husband's friend. I think the worst moment was when she kicked me out of our bed that we'd shared for 43 years saying I wasn't her husband. So I got two single beds and pushed them together so she's still in her own bed. I couldn't put her in a home. How could you after all those years together? Some people wouldn't or couldn't put up with this, I know. But you have to be patient and if I get irritable I just go out of the room. I have no choice, this is my duty because she is my wife. I do get satisfactions. I like to make her as happy as possible and do things to please her. I'd sooner have her here this way than not at all. We're great pals now, we're not lovers. It hurts, but it's a question of having to accept it the way it is.'

Helpful organizations and further reading

Chapter 1
Carers National Association
21–23 New Road
Chatham
Kent ME4 4QJ
Tel 0634 813981
and
29 Chilworth Mews
London W2 3RG
Tel 01-262 1451

Family Welfare Association
501–505 Kingsland Road
London E8 4AU
Tel 01-241 1580

Council and Care for the Elderly
131 Middlesex Street
London E1 7JF
Tel 01-621 1624

Age Concern England
Bernard Sunley House
60 Pitcairn Road
Mitcham
Surrey CR4 3LL
Tel 01-640 5431

Chapter 2
National Association of Citizens Advice Bureaux
115 Pentonville Road
London N1
Tel 01-833 2181

National Federation of Housing Associations
175 Grays Inn Road
London WC1
Tel 01-833 8322

GRACE (Goulds Residential Advisory Centre for the Elderly)
PO Box 71
Cobham
Surrey KT11 2JR
Tel 0932 62928

Elderly Accommodation Council
1 Durwood House
31 Kensington Court
London W8
Tel 01-937 8709

The Registered Nursing Homes Association
74 Portland Place
London W1N 4AN
Tel 01-631 1524

College of Health
2 Marylebone Road
London NW1 4DX
Tel 01-935 3251

Abbeyfield Society
35a High Street
Potters Bar
Hertfordshire
Tel 0707 51774

National Association of Almshouses
Billingbear Lodge
Wokingham
Berkshire RG11 5RU

Standing Conference of Ethnic Minority Senior Citizens
5 Westminster Bridge Road
London SE1
Tel 01-928 0095

Equal Opportunities Commission
Overseas House
Quay Street
Manchester M3 3HN
Tel 061-833 9244

British Red Cross
9 Grosvenor Crescent
London SW1
Tel 01-235 5454

Crossroads
94 Coton Road
Rugby
Warwickshire CV21 4LN
Tel 0788 73653

Community Service Volunteers
237 Pentonville Road
London N1
Tel 01-278 6601

Chapter 3
Wirelesses for the Bedridden Society
81b Corbets Tey Road
Upminster
Essex
Tel 040-22 50051

Disabled Living Foundation
380–384 Harrow Road
London W9 2HU
Tel 01-289 6111

Royal Association for Disability and Rehabilitation (RADAR)
25 Mortimer Street
London W1N 8AB
Tel 01-637 5400

National Aids for the Disabled Exhibition (Naidex)
90 Calverley Road,
Tunbridge Wells,
Kent TN1 2UN
Tel 0892 44027

Royal Society for the Prevention of Accidents (ROSPA)
1 Grosvenor Crescent
London SW1
Tel 01-235 6889

Help the Aged
16–18 St James Walk
London EC1R 0BE
Tel 01-253 0253

Pensioners Link
17 Balfe Street
London N1 9EB
Tel 01-278 5501

Health Education Authority
78 New Oxford Street
London WC1
Tel 01-631 0930

Exploring Living Memory
42 Queen Square
London WC1N 3AJ
Tel 01-405 9704

Age Exchange Reminiscence Centre
11 Blackheath Village
London SE3
Tel 01-318 9105

Extend
3 The Boulevard
Sheringham
Norfolk NR26 8LJ

Nutrition Education Service
Sussex House
Burgess Hill
West Sussex RH15 9AW

Chapter 4
The Patients Association
18 Charing Cross Road
London WC2
Tel 01-240 0671

Chest, Heart and Stroke Association (CHSA)
Tavistock House North
London WC1H 9JE
Tel 01-387 3012

VOCAL
336 Brixton Road
London SW9 7AA
Tel 01-274 4029

Parkinson's Disease Society
36 Portland Place
London W1N 3DG
Tel 01-323 1174

Arthritis Care
6 Grosvenor Crescent
London SW1
Tel 01-235 0902

Arthritis and Rheumatism Council
41 Eagle Street
London WC1 4AR
Tel 01-405 8572

Cancerlink
46 Pentonville Road
London N1 9HF
Tel 01-833 2451

British Association of Cancer United Patients (BACUP)
121–123 Charterhouse Street
London EC1M 6AA
Tel 01-608 1661

Alzheimer's Disease Society
Bank Buildings
Fulham Broadway
London SW6 1EP
Tel 01-381 3177

Multiple Sclerosis Society (MS)
386 Munster Road
Fulham
London SW6 6AP
Tel 01-381 4022

Motor Neurone Disease Association
38 Hazelwood Road
Northampton NN1 1LN
Tel 0604 22269

Volunteer Stroke Scheme
7 Albion Street
London W2 2AS
Tel 01-262 8385

Colostomy Welfare Group
38 Eccleston Square
London SW1
Tel 01-828 5175

National Eczema Society
Tavistock House North
Tavistock Square
London WC1H 9SR
Tel 01-388 4097

St John's Ambulance
1 Grosvenor Crescent
London SW1
Tel 01-235 5231

British Red Cross
(See under Chapter 2)

National Association for Mental Health (MIND)
22 Harley Street
London W1
Tel 01-637 0741

Chapter 5
Royal National Institute for the Deaf (RNID)
105 Gower Street
London WC1E 6AH
Tel 01-387 8033

British Talking Book Service for the Blind
Nuffield Library
Mount Pleasant
Wembley
Middlesex HAQ 1RR
Tel 01-903 6666

National Listening Library
12 Lant Street
London SE1
Tel 01-407 9417

Talking Newspaper Association
48 Leigh Road
Eastleigh
Hampshire
Tel 0703-641 244

British Telephones for the Blind
Mynhurst Leigh
Near Reigate
Surrey

Royal National Institute for the Blind (RNIB)
224 Great Portland Street
London W1N 6AA
Tel 01-388 1266

Wireless for the Blind Fund
As above

Action for Dysphasic Adults (ADA)
Northcote House
37a Royal Street
London SE1 7LL
Tel 01-261 9572

Exploring Living Memory
See under Chapter 3

Age Exchange
See under Chapter 3

RECALL
Help the Aged: See under Chapter 3

Contact
18 Henrietta Street
London WC2E QQH
Tel 01-240 0630

Society for Companion Animal Studies (SCAS)
4th Floor
Walter House
418–422 Strand
London WC2R 0PL
Tel 01-240 6911

Chapter 6
Yoga for Health Foundation
9 Old Bond Street
London W1X 3TA
Tel 01-493 0165

British Wheel of Yoga
Grafton Grange
Grafton
York YO5 9QQ
Tel 09012 3386

Society of Teachers of the Alexander Technique
3b Albert Court
Kensington Gore
London SW7
Tel 01-584 3834

Relaxation for Living
29 Burwood Park Road
Walton-on-Thames
Surrey KT12 5LH
Tel 0932 27826

Open University Community Education Courses
Walton Hall
Milton Keynes
Buckinghamshire MK7 6AA
Tel 0908 653791

Cruse
Cruse House
126 Sheen Road
Richmond
Surrey TW9 1UR
Tel 01-940 4818

National Association of Widows
Chell Road
Stafford
Staffordshire ST16 2QA
Tel 0785 45465

MIND
See under Chapter 4

Chapter 7
Disability Alliance
25 Denmark Street
London WC2H 8NJ
Tel 01-240 0806

Centre for Policy on Ageing
25 Ironmonger Row
London EC1V 3QP
Tel 01-253 1787

Mobility Information Services
Copthorne Community Hall
Shelton Road
Shrewsbury
Shropshire S73 8DT
Tel 0743 68383

Council and Care for the Elderly
See under Chapter 1

Age Concern England
See under Chapter 2

Chapter 8
Women's Royal Voluntary Service
17 Old Park Lane
London W1Y 4AJ
Tel 01-499 6040

Contact
See under Chapter 5

Crossroads
See under Chapter 2

Standing Conference of Ethnic Minorities
See under Chapter 2

Further reading and sources of information
Action for Carers
A guide for local carer groups,
available from:
Age Concern, Greater London
54 Knatchbull Road
London SE5 9QY
Tel 01-737 3456

Activities for the Frail Elderly
Available with other publications on reminiscence therapy
from Winslow Press, 23 Horn Street, Winslow,
Buckinghamshire MK18 3AP (Freephone 3650)

Assert Yourself Gail Lindenfield (Thorsons, 1987)

A Stroke in the Family by Valerie Eaten Griffith (Wildwood
House, 1975)

Care Attendant Schemes
Describes setting up a Care Attendant Scheme. Available from GLAD, 336 Brixton Road, London SW9 7AA (Tel 01-274 0107)

Caring: Experiences of Looking After a Disabled Relative, Anna Briggs and Judith Oliver (Routledge & Kegan Paul, 1985)

Caring for Older People
This is an Open University course for carers (see under Chapter 6 for address)

Caring for Your Elderly Relative, M. Keith Thompson (Martin Dunitz: MacDonald Orbis, 1986)

Community Care Project Newsletter
Available from the National Council for Voluntary Organizations, 26 Bedford Square, London WC1B 3HU (Tel 01-636 4066)

Coping with Ageing Parents, Chris Gilleard and Glenda Watt (MacDonald, 1983)

Dementia and Mental Illness, Elaine Murphy (Papermac, 1986)

Elderly People: Rights and Opportunities, Jill Manthorpe, (Longmans, 1986)

Family Care of Old People, Tim Dartington (Souvenir Press, 1980)

Family Care of the Handicapped Elderly: Who Pays? Policy Studies Institute, available from the Carers National Association (see under Chapter 1 for address)

In Our Care
Training pack and practical guide to groups of carers from Help the Aged (see under Chapter 3 for address)

Intensive Home Help and Home Care Services
Examples of services for carers of elderly people in various parts of the country. Available, along with many other publications including *Sharing Your Home* and *A Buyer's Guide to Sheltered Housing*, from Age Concern England (see under Chapter 1 for address)

Keeping Fit While Caring, Christine Darby
Available from the Family Welfare Association (see under Chapter 1 for address)

Old and Healthy
A Thames TV *Help!* programme publication available from Ember House, 164-166 Drummond Street, London NW1 3HU (Tel 01-387 9494)

Practising Community Care
All about developing locally-based schemes. Available from Community Care, Carew House, Wallington, Surrey SM6 (Tel 01-661 3500)

Starting a Self-help Group
Part of pack from the Agewell Campaign, available from Age Concern England (see under Chapter 1 for address)

Taking a Break
Free booklet describing over 20 types of relief care, available along with other helpful publications from Kings Fund, 126 Albert Centre, London NW1 (Tel 01-267 6111)

Take Care of Your Elderly Relative, Dr Muir Gray (Allen & Unwin, 1980)

Tapes for Relaxing
Available from New World Cassettes, Strawberry Vale, Twickenham, TW1 1BR (Tel 01-892 3839)

The Legal Status of Residents in Shared Housing Schemes
Available from the National Federation of Housing Associations (see under Chapter 2 for address)

36-hour Day, Nancy L. Mace, et al (Hodder & Stoughton, 1985)

Triple Jeopardy: growing old in a second homeland,
Available from the Centre for Policy on Ageing (see under Chapter 7 for address)

Daughters Who Care, Jane Lewis and Barbara Meredith (Routledge, 1988)

Index